Penguin Readers

NINETEEN EIGHTY-FOUR

GEORGE ORWELL

D1637774

LEVEL

RETOLD BY FIONA MACKENZIE
SERIES EDITOR: SORREL PITTS

PENGUIN BOOKS
UK | USA | Canada | Ireland | Australia
India | New Zealand | South Africa

Penguin Books is part of the Penguin Random House group of companies
whose addresses can be found at global.penguinrandomhouse.com.
www.penguin.co.uk   www.puffin.co.uk   www.ladybird.co.uk

Nineteen Eighty-Four first published by Martin Secker & Warburg Ltd, 1949
Penguin Readers edition of *Nineteen Eighty-Four* published by Penguin Books Ltd, 2020

001

Original text written by George Orwell
Text for Penguin Readers edition adapted by Fiona Mackenzie
Text for Penguin Readers edition copyright © Penguin Books Ltd, 2020
Illustration Courtesy of Shepard Fairey/obeygiant.com

Set in 11/16 pt Baskerville
Typeset by Jouve (UK), Milton Keynes
Printed and bound in Great Britain by Clays Ltd, Elcograf S.p.A.

A CIP catalogue record for this book is available from the British Library

ISBN: 978-0-2414-3097-2

All correspondence to:
Penguin Books
Penguin Random House Children's
One Embassy Gardens, New Union Square
5 Nine Elms Lane, London SW8 5DA

Contents

Note about the story   7

Nineteen Eighty-Four glossary   8

Before-reading questions   9

Chapter One – At Victory House   11

Chapter Two – Greetings to the future   17

Chapter Three – Newspeak and doublethink   22

Chapter Four – Dead men and living men   28

Chapter Five – Two plus two make four   35

Chapter Six – The shop   40

Chapter Seven – I love you   46

Chapter Eight – Julia   51

Chapter Nine – A love song and a rat   57

Chapter Ten – O'Brien   62

Chapter Eleven – The proles are human beings   67

Chapter Twelve – The Brotherhood   71

Chapter Thirteen – The book   76

Chapter Fourteen – The Thought Police   80

Chapter Fifteen – The Ministry of Love   84

Chapter Sixteen – *Freedom is slavery – slavery is freedom*   93

Chapter Seventeen – Room 101   99

Chapter Eighteen – *2 + 2 = 5*   104

During-reading questions   108

After-reading questions   111

Exercises   112

Project work   118

Essay questions   120

Glossary   121

Note about the story

George Orwell is the author of two of the most famous novels in the English language – *Nineteen Eighty-Four* and *Animal Farm* (also available in Penguin Readers at Level 3). *Nineteen Eighty-Four* is a novel about a 'dystopia' – an imagined society where everything is more stupid, **savage*** and frightening than in the real world.

Orwell (1903–1950) wrote *Nineteen Eighty-Four* just after the Second World War (1939–1945). He did not intend it to be an accurate picture of what he thought the year 1984 would be like in Britain. In fact, his novel is a satire – a book which shows what he thought was wrong with the world in his own day, in the middle of the twentieth century.

The world in *Nineteen Eighty-Four* is divided into three areas – Oceania, Eurasia and Eastasia, which are always at war. Orwell never tells us exactly which countries are in each area, but we can make guesses from their names. Winston Smith, the main character, lives in Airstrip One (Britain), in Oceania, which is ruled by the **Party** and its leader, Big Brother.

* Definitions of words in **bold** can be found in the glossary on pages 121-126.

Nineteen-Eighty Four glossary

Some of the words that Orwell invented – for example, *doublethink* and *Room 101* – have become part of modern English. These words are usually used in a negative way, although *Big Brother* is also the name of a popular **reality** TV programme, which shows in public what people usually do in private.

Airstrip One	the name for Britain in 1984
doublethink	holding two opposite opinions at the same time
facecrime	when your face shows that you are thinking something bad
Newspeak	the official language of Oceania, which contains no unnecessary words
Oldspeak	the old English language, before Newspeak
speakwrite	a machine that types what a person says
telescreen	a two-way video screen
thoughtcrime	thinking something against the Party; and a person guilty of a thoughtcrime is a thought-criminal

Before-reading questions

1 Explain what you know about George Orwell. If you do not know anything about him, what would you like to know?

2 George Orwell finished writing *Nineteen Eighty-Four* in 1948. What is the connection between these two dates, do you think? What do the dates tell you about the kind of story this is?

3 Look at the list of chapter titles. Choose the five titles that you think sound most interesting and say why.

CHAPTER ONE
At Victory House

It was a bright cold day in April, and the clocks were **striking** thirteen. Winston Smith went quickly through the glass doors of **Victory** House to get out of the horrible wind, which blew **dust** into the building with him. The hall smelled of boiled cabbage and at the end of it there was a huge poster. It showed the enormous face of a handsome man with a big black moustache.

Winston went up the stairs. It was no use trying the lift. It was often broken, but at the moment there was no electricity during the day because the **Party** was saving money in order to pay for Hate Week. Winston's flat was on the seventh floor, and Winston, who was thirty-nine and not very healthy, had to rest several times on the way up. He was a small, thin man who looked thinner because of the large blue **overalls** which were his uniform as an unimportant member of the **Outer** Party. His hair was fair and the skin on his face was rough because of the old **razor blades** he had to use when he shaved.

As Winston went up the stairs, on each floor, opposite the lift, the poster with the enormous face looked at him from the wall. The eyes seemed to watch him. The words underneath the picture said: BIG BROTHER IS WATCHING YOU.

Inside his flat, a voice was speaking from the telescreen, which was part of the wall on the right of the door. Winston pressed a button so the screen became less bright and the voice became quieter, but it was impossible to turn it off. He moved over to the window and looked out over London. Everywhere looked grey and colourless, except for the posters, which were attached to most of the buildings. The brown eyes looked at Winston: BIG BROTHER IS WATCHING YOU. Another poster, with a torn corner, moved in the wind, showing and then hiding the name of the Party, INGSOC. A helicopter flew close to the windows of flats so the police **patrol** could see what the people inside were doing. Winston did not care what the police patrol did. It was the Thought Police who worried him. Through the telescreen, the Thought Police could hear every sound and see every move Winston made. In fact, they could hear and see every Party member through the telescreens in each of their homes. Everyone knew that all the sounds they made were listened to and all their movements were watched.

From his window, Winston could see the huge white building of the **Ministry** of Truth, where he worked. 'Minitrue', as it was called in Newspeak, the official language of Oceania, was a modern building compared with the tired, **dusty** city all around it. London was the main city of Airstrip One, in Oceania. Winston tried hard to remember if London had always been like this, but it was no use. No memories of how it used to be when he was a child came back to him.

The Ministry of Truth managed news, education and culture. And from where he stood, Winston could also see the buildings of the other three ministries which ruled Oceania: the Ministry of Peace, which controlled war, the Ministry of Plenty, which controlled economics, and the Ministry of Love, which managed the law. 'Minipax', 'Miniplenty' and 'Miniluv' were their names in Newspeak. It was the enormous, windowless building of Miniluv which Winston feared most. There were high fences around the building and guards in black uniforms with guns, and no one ever went in there except on official business.

Winston turned away from the window and went to the tiny kitchen. As he passed the telescreen, he made sure his face looked calm and optimistic, in case anyone was watching. He was going to miss his lunch in the **canteen**, having left the Ministry at this time of day, and there was no food in his kitchen except the piece of brown bread which was tomorrow's breakfast. He took a bottle from a cupboard. It had a plain label saying 'Victory **Gin**' and, when Winston took the top off, there was a horrible oily smell. He half-filled a teacup with it, took a deep breath and drank the alcohol as if it was medicine. His face went red, tears ran out of his eyes and he felt as if he had been hit on the head. When the shock had passed, however, he started to feel a bit happier.

Winston then went to an **alcove** to the right of the telescreen. The alcove had probably been intended as a place to keep books when the flats were built. It was a place where he could sit without the telescreen being able to see him, although of course it could still hear him. He sat down and looked at something which he had just bought in a shop in a poor area of the city. It was a beautiful notebook with empty white pages. Even with nothing written in it, it could get him into trouble. But what he was going to do with it could get him **executed**. People had not used pens very much since the speakwrite had been invented, but Winston had found an old one. He opened the book and wrote untidily at the top of the first page: *4th April 1984.* Winston had decided to write a diary – though he was not sure who it was for. He could not imagine a time in the future when anyone would be able to read it. He had planned for weeks to do this, to write down the thoughts that had been in his head for years. But now, with the empty white paper in front of him, his thoughts had gone.

Suddenly, he started writing about a recent visit to the cinema, where there had been films of people being injured and killed, which the audience, including himself, had laughed at. He did not know why he was writing about that. He wrote very fast, but he had to stop because of the pain in his hand – he was not used to writing.

Then he remembered something unusual which had happened at the Ministry that morning, when he and the other workers in the **Records Department** had stood in front of the telescreen for the Daily Hate. He did not often look at the people there, but this morning he had noticed two of them who were sitting close to him. One was a pretty, dark-haired young woman who worked in the **Fiction** Department. She wore the red scarf of the **Anti-**Sex Society and Winston felt afraid of her because most young women were wildly enthusiastic about the Party and often **spied** on their neighbours for the Thought Police. She had arrived that morning at the same time as a man called O'Brien, a member of the **Inner** Party. Winston had seen O'Brien sometimes over the years and felt connected to him – he felt that O'Brien, like him, was not enthusiastic about the Party.

As usual, the Daily Hate had been against Goldstein.

Goldstein had once been an important Party member but now he was Big Brother's greatest enemy, although no one remembered why. There were stories that Goldstein led a group called the Brotherhood, which wanted to **overthrow** the Party. On the telescreen, Goldstein was shouting, demanding peace with Eurasia, which Oceania and Eastasia were at war with.

In front of the telescreen, all the workers had become angry and were starting to shout at Goldstein. Then the dark-haired young woman threw her Newspeak Dictionary at the screen and everyone began shouting louder. Winston found that he was shouting, too, and kicking his chair. He remembered how easy it was to become really angry during the Daily Hate – he did not have to act. But this morning his hate was directed against Big Brother himself, the Party and the Thought Police, and then against the dark-haired young woman. He had suddenly felt very angry with her – a horrible, violent anger.

After the Hate had finished, Goldstein's face had been replaced on the screen by the three Party **slogans**:

WAR IS PEACE
FREEDOM IS **SLAVERY**
IGNORANCE IS STRENGTH

and the workers had shouted "B-B, B-B" over and over again. O'Brien had stood up to leave and as he did, he had looked at Winston. In that moment, Winston had again felt connected to him. "I am with you, I am on your side," O'Brien seemed to be saying to him, as if they shared feelings against the Party.

Winston came back to the present and realized that he had written *DOWN WITH BIG BROTHER* five times in big letters on the page. Terrible fear came over him. For a moment he thought about tearing the page from his diary. But he knew it was useless – it would make no difference, because in the end the Thought Police would arrest him. He imagined them knocking on his door at night. He began to write quickly: *THEY'LL SHOOT ME IN THE BACK OF THE NECK.*

Suddenly there was a knock on the door. Was it the Thought Police already? Winston moved slowly towards the door. Although his heart was jumping wildly, years of practice had taught him to keep his face calm.

CHAPTER TWO

Greetings to the future

After Winston had breathed deeply to make himself calmer, then carefully opened the door, he quickly relaxed. A woman with a tired face and thin grey-brown hair stood there.

"Oh, **Comrade**," she said, in a tiny, worried voice. "Could you look at our kitchen sink? The water won't go down and . . ." Her voice became quieter and quieter till she stopped speaking completely.

It was Mrs Parsons, who lived on the same floor as Winston. She was about thirty, but she looked much older. Winston was not surprised by her visit. The flats in Victory House were old and falling to pieces – ceilings, walls and water **pipes** often had holes in them, and the heating did not work very well. Flats were never repaired for them, so people repaired their own and each other's if they could.

"Tom would do it if he was at home . . ." said Mrs Parsons, as Winston followed her along the corridor to her flat. Tom, her husband, a worker at Minitrue with Winston, was the kind of stupid person who the Party liked. He never asked questions. The Parsons had two children, so their flat was bigger than Winston's. On the way to the kitchen Winston saw on the walls the **banners** of the **Spies**, an organization which all children belonged to, as well as a poster of Big Brother. He could hear military music from the telescreen in the living room as they passed it and he could also hear someone trying to play the music on a comb and paper.

"It's the children," said Mrs Parsons, nervously. "They haven't been out today so they . . ." She always talked quietly and her sentences never really finished. However, Winston knew that almost all the parents in Oceania were afraid of their children. The Thought Police encouraged children to **spy** on their parents and report anything they did or said which was against Party rules.

The sink was filled with dirty green water which smelled horribly of cabbage. Winston bent down to find where two pipes were joined beneath the sink. The movement made his back hurt. "Have you got any tools I can use?" he asked.

"Tools . . ." she said. "Oh, I don't know. Perhaps the children . . ." She wandered away and came back with a bag of tools, then wandered away again to the living room where the noise of the children was becoming even louder. Winston took apart the pipes and let the water out, removing a lot of horrible, smelly human hair. He cleaned his fingers as well as he could in cold water from the tap and went to the living room.

"Put your hands up!" shouted a **savage** voice. A boy of nine was pointing a toy gun at Winston. Behind him stood a small girl about two years younger, who was doing the same thing with a piece of wood. Both of them were wearing the uniform of the Spies – blue shorts, grey shirts and red scarves.

"You're a thought-criminal!" screamed the boy. "You're a Eurasian criminal! I'll shoot you! I'll **vaporize** you!"

The boy and girl jumped around Winston shouting,

"Thought-criminal!" The boy sounded so savage that Winston felt glad he was not holding a real gun.

Mrs Parsons looked nervously from Winston to the children and back again. "They get so noisy," she said. "They're disappointed because they can't go to the **hanging**, you see. I'm too busy and Tom is at work so . . ."

"Why can't we go to the hanging?" shouted the boy.

"Want to see the hanging!" screamed the little girl.

Winston remembered that some Eurasian prisoners were going to be hanged in a park that evening. Children enjoyed watching these public hangings, which happened every month.

He said goodbye to Mrs Parsons, and as he walked down the corridor, he felt a sharp pain as a stone hit the back of his neck. He turned round quickly, in time to see Mrs Parsons dragging the boy back into the flat.

"Goldstein!" the boy screamed at him.

Winston saw the look of helpless fear on the mother's pale, tired face. Belonging to the Spies made the children love the Party and Big Brother more than their parents. The organization was just a game to them, as they sang songs, shouted slogans and marched with guns. But they became savage and learned to hate all the people who were called 'enemies of the Party,' like foreigners. They were **praised** and called 'child heroes' in newspaper **articles** if they told the Thought Police when their parents had done something wrong.

As soon as he was back in his own flat, Winston sat down in the alcove again and picked up his pen. But before he could continue writing, he suddenly thought about O'Brien again.

About seven years ago, Winston had had a dream. He was walking through a dark room when he heard a voice say quietly, "*We shall meet in the place where there is no darkness.*" At the time, the words had not seemed important, but as the years had passed, he had become sure that it was O'Brien's voice which spoke. Winston was certain that there was a link between the two of them. He did not know whether they were friends or enemies and it did not matter. "*We shall meet in the place where there is no darkness,*" O'Brien had said, and Winston knew that in some way this would come true.

Suddenly, loud music came from the telescreen, followed by a voice announcing a wonderful victory by Oceanian soldiers in South India. And there was bad news. "And now, here is a newsflash . . ." said the voice. "The chocolate **ration** is being reduced from thirty **grams** to twenty." Then the Oceanian **national anthem** started to play very loudly. *Oceania, my dear land* . . . it started, and Winston stood up, as he had to do whenever it was played.

When the anthem had ended, he went back to the window. Far away, he heard a rocket bomb explode as it landed. About twenty or thirty of them landed on London every day.

The past was dead and he could not imagine the future. Would anyone ever remember a time before the Party? Would the Party last forever? He took a coin from his pocket and looked at the Party slogans on one side and the head of Big Brother on the other. Even from the coin, the eyes were looking at him. He felt alone. Was there anyone on his side?

The clocks struck fourteen, and Winston had to be back at

work in the Ministry by fourteen-thirty. But before he left, he added some more lines to his diary and felt less **pessimistic**:

*Greetings to the future, to a time when thought is free, when men are different from each other and do not live alone. Greetings to a time when truth **exists** and cannot be changed.*

He was already dead, he thought, because he had started to explain his thoughts. Then he wrote: Thoughtcrime does not lead to death. Thoughtcrime IS death.

Now he knew that he was a dead man, it was important to stay alive as long as possible. So, before he went back to work, he used a piece of rough brown soap to wash away the ink marks from the fingers that had held the pen.

CHAPTER THREE

Newspeak and doublethink

That night Winston dreamed about his mother. She had disappeared when he was about ten years old. He believed that she must have been killed, together with his father and sister, at a time the Party was executing hundreds of people who disagreed with its plans. In his dream, Winston's mother was sitting with a tiny baby, his sister, in her arms. Slowly, his mother and sister moved further and further away from him. Winston knew that soon they would disappear forever and that he was responsible. He also remembered that they had loved him, something that could not happen in 1984, a time when nobody cared about anybody else.

Next he dreamed about a place he often visited in his dreams – a peaceful place with fields and trees, and a small, slow-moving river. He called it the Golden Country when he was thinking about it, though he did not know if it was a real place he had once seen. In his dream, the dark-haired young woman from the Fiction Department was coming towards him, taking off all her clothes. Winston did not desire her young, naked body. He just admired her. By throwing away her clothes, she showed that she rejected Big Brother, the Party, the Thought Police and everything else which ruled their lives.

He woke up as the telescreen made a loud, horrible noise. It was time for office workers like Winston to get up. In three minutes he had to be in front of the telescreen ready for the morning exercises. He put on his dirty **underwear** and shorts, and suddenly started to cough so much that he could not breathe. This happened every morning and he had to lie on the bed again until the coughing stopped.

"Thirty to forty group!" shouted a loud female voice. "Take your places!" This was Winston's age group and he knew that he had to be seen in front of the telescreen during the exercises.

A young woman with strong muscles, dressed in gym clothes, had already appeared on the telescreen when Winston jumped in front of it.

"Bend and stretch your arms," she shouted. "Copy me. One, two, three, four! Come on! Move!"

As she shouted at him to do the exercises, Winston's dream came back to him and he found himself trying to think about when he was a boy. However, he could remember almost nothing before the late 1950s and he knew there were no history books which could help him. This was because history was always changing. But Winston knew that everything had been different in the early 1950s. The maps were different then. Countries had different names. Airstrip One had been called England or Britain, for example, but he thought that London had always been called London.

As the exercises continued, Winston remembered that once there had been peace, but then something so terrible had happened that there had never been peace again. He had a confused memory of the day the first rocket bomb fell on an English city. He remembered holding his father's hand and running along streets, then going down deep into the earth, into an underground station where there were hundreds of frightened people. Since then there had always been war, though he was sure it had not always been the same war. The Party said now that Oceania had always been at war with Eurasia. But Winston was certain that four years ago, Oceania had been fighting on the same side as Eurasia against Eastasia. He knew he could not prove this because the Party was rewriting history all the time, destroying old history books and replacing them with new ones. In this way, the Party's lies became truth. This control of **reality** by the Party was called 'doublethink' in Newspeak. The Party required everyone to use doublethink to change their memories, and it used another slogan to remind them: "*Whoever controls the past controls the future; whoever controls the present controls the past.*"

"Take a rest!" shouted the gym teacher. Winston put his arms by his sides and took deep breaths, and while he rested, he continued to think about doublethink. It was the ability to have two different opinions about the same thing at the same time, believing both of them to be true. To understand the word doublethink, you had to use doublethink.

"Right!" shouted the teacher. "Let's bend over and touch our toes. One, two! One, two! Don't bend your knees!" Winston hated this exercise because it made his back hurt and often made him cough. He tried to touch his toes without bending his knees, while trying to remember when he had first seen the name Big Brother and the word INGSOC, the name of the Party. He thought that it was in about 1960 and that INGSOC was the Newspeak name for the Oldspeak name 'English **Socialism**', although the past had been rewritten so he could not be sure. There were some things, however, which he was certain were lies. For example, the Party history books said the Party had invented aeroplanes, but he could remember seeing planes when he was a very young child.

Suddenly the teacher's voice screamed from the telescreen, "6079 Comrade Smith W, you aren't trying hard enough! Bend lower!" Winston felt himself **sweating** with fear, but his face still looked calm.

"Don't look upset or angry," he said to himself. "Never let them see what you're thinking or feeling." His back and his legs hurt, but finally he managed to touch his toes without bending his knees.

———

Soon after his exercises, Winston, in his Party uniform, arrived at his desk at the Records Department in Minitrue, sat down and pulled his speakwrite towards him. His desk was in a small **cubicle**, which was one of many along both sides of a long corridor. In his cubicle, as well as the desk and the speakwrite, there were a telescreen and two tubes, a small one and a large one. **Instructions** about the work Winston had to do came out of the small tube and newspapers came out of the larger tube. Next to the desk there was a hole for wastepaper. There were similar holes in every room and every corridor in the building. They were known by Winston and the other workers as 'memory holes' because all the paper you put into them was immediately burned in a huge **furnace** so the memory of what was on it did not exist any more.

Four notes came out of the small tube. They instructed

Winston about **corrections** which had to be made to reports in newspapers and other documents. Three of them were simple corrections, but the fourth was a more difficult one. Winston felt pleased because this was the kind of work he enjoyed. He put the fourth note at the side of his desk to do last, and looked again at the first note. It was about a correction which had to be made to an article in the *Times* newspaper from the previous month. Winston used the telescreen to order a copy of the newspaper, which came out of the larger tube a few minutes later.

The newspaper reported that Big Brother had said an attack by Eurasian soldiers on Oceanian soldiers would take place in North Africa, and that South India would remain peaceful. In reality, the opposite had happened. Big Brother could not be wrong, so reality had to change. Winston quickly spoke the words of a new article into his speakwrite, printed it and attached the new article to the newspaper. Then he put the newspaper into the larger tube and put his instruction into the memory hole, so it would be burned in the furnace.

Winston knew what would happen next. Someone in another part of Minitrue would make a new **edition** of the newspaper, including his rewritten paragraph, print it and file it. The old version would be destroyed, so no copies of it would remain. And soon, another new edition would be required. Changing the past was extremely important work for Minitrue, so many of those who worked there spent all their time finding copies of newspapers, books, articles, photographs and anything else from the past which could disagree with today's truth. Once they had been found and changed, the original copies would be thrown into the furnace. Other workers, in the Fiction Department, spent their days rewriting novels, poems, pictures, articles, films, and plays so that they all contained only the most recent thoughts of the Party and Big Brother.

Having finished this first correction, Winston completed the second and third corrections quickly. Then it was time for the Daily Hate.

CHAPTER FOUR
Dead men and living men

When the Daily Hate was over, Winston started his fourth job. The note said: "*times 3.12.83 bb rpt doubleplusungood abt unperson rewrite full upsend antefiling*". He knew immediately that in Oldspeak the note meant: "*The report of Big Brother's speech in the* Times newspaper *of 3rd December 1983 is extremely bad because it is about someone who has never existed. Rewrite it completely and send it to a manager to be checked before you file the article.*"

'Unpersons' were people who had been vaporized. They had been killed and all information about them had been removed from anywhere it might be found. The result was that they had never existed. Winston's job today was difficult because the article in the *Times* was about a speech by Big Brother which praised an unperson. This was the kind of interesting work which Winston enjoyed most and he felt proud that he had been given such a difficult job.

Winston used the telescreen to order a copy of the *Times* newspaper and found the article. It was about a man called Comrade Withers who had been awarded a medal by Big Brother because he had done such good work for the Party. Winston would never know what Withers had done wrong. People often disappeared. Winston could remember about thirty people, including his parents and sister, who had disappeared. Usually these people were dead. Sometimes they reappeared after a number of years.

"I won't keep the existing article," thought Winston. "I'll

invent a new Party member for Big Brother to praise. His name will be Comrade Ogilvy."

Then he noticed that a man called Tillotson, who worked in the cubicle on the other side of the corridor, was looking at him in an unfriendly way.

"He must have been given the same job as me," thought Winston suddenly. He did not mind, as it was normal for important jobs to be given to lots of people. The managers would choose the best piece of work.

Winston pulled the speakwrite towards him and started the new article as if Big Brother was speaking. *What kind of man was Comrade Ogilvy? At the age of three, he refused all toys except for a machine gun. At the age of six, he became a leader of the Spies and at nine, he* **denounced** *his uncle to the Thought Police. At the age of nineteen, he became an organizer in the Anti-Sex Society. Then he designed a special bomb which killed thirty-one Eurasian prisoners at the same time. And now, Comrades, Comrade Ogilvy, at the age of twenty-three, is dead! He died saving Oceania from its enemies. What can we learn from his life, Comrades? We can learn that we should all live lives like his!*

Winston continued the article with more **praise** from Big Brother. Comrade Ogilvy became one of the best members the Party had ever had. However, Winston decided not to award any medals to Ogilvy because there would have to be information about them in other documents as well as in the *Times*. Mistakes might be made.

Winston was proud of his article and he felt sure his managers would prefer his article to Tillotson's.

Later, when Winston was waiting to collect his lunch in the noisy canteen, he heard a voice behind him.

"You're just the man I was looking for," a man said. It was Winston's friend, Syme, although nobody really had friends these days. "Have you got any razor blades?" continued Syme, a man with a thin, dark face.

"No, I haven't. I've been using the same blade for the last two weeks," replied Winston, lying. Often, for weeks, people could not buy things they needed, and at the moment there were no razor blades in the Party shops. Winston had two, which he wanted to keep for himself.

Winston and Syme each picked up a dirty tray.

"Did you go to the hangings of the prisoners yesterday?" asked Syme.

"No, I couldn't. I was working," replied Winston. Syme was an enthusiastic Party member, and it was not safe for him to know how much Winston hated public hangings. It was safer to talk to Syme about his work on the Newspeak Dictionary.

"Next, please!" shouted a female prole. Syme and Winston put their trays on the **shelf** in front of her and she put on each one a bowl of watery pink-coloured stuff, a thick piece of bread, a small piece of cheese and a mug of Victory coffee without milk or sugar. It was the usual lunch.

"There's a table over there, under that telescreen," said Syme. "Let's get a gin on the way."

They picked up teacups of Victory Gin and made their way across the busy canteen to a dirty metal table.

"How's your work going?" asked Winston.

Syme was always enthusiastic about the dictionary.

"It's going slowly," he said. "But it's really interesting. The eleventh edition of the dictionary is going to be the one which completes the language of Newspeak. You probably think that the most important work we do is to invent new words. But in fact the most important thing is destroying Oldspeak words – we're destroying hundreds of them every day. Soon, there will only be the words we need and people like you will need to learn Newspeak all over again. Oldspeak won't exist."

Syme finished his meal, then he continued talking enthusiastically about the dictionary. "I'm working on the adjectives. Think about the word 'bad'. Why do we need it? We don't, because each word can be used to make its own opposite. If something is 'good', its opposite is 'ungood'. What's the use of having words like 'excellent' when we can say 'plusgood' or even 'doubleplusgood'? We use these words now with the Oldspeak ones, but when we have finished the dictionary there will only be six words for goodness and badness." Then he quickly added, "It is all BB's idea, of course."

Winston tried to look interested when he heard Big Brother's name, but Syme noticed that his interest was not real.

"You don't really understand the importance of Newspeak," he said almost sadly. "You think in Oldspeak before you write in Newspeak. You like the old, untidy words, don't you?"

Winston smiled, not wanting to speak, and Syme continued. "Newspeak is the only language which is getting smaller every year. Thoughtcrime will become impossible because there will be no words to explain any ideas except the correct ones. Do you realize that by 2050, no one will be able to understand the conversation we're having now?"

"Except the proles," Winston thought, but he did not say it, feeling it might be a thoughtcrime.

It seemed as if Syme had guessed what Winston was thinking. "The proles aren't really people," Syme said. "By 2050, or earlier even, all real knowledge of Oldspeak will have disappeared. Even the Party's books and slogans will change. How could you have a slogan like 'Freedom is slavery' when nobody knows what freedom is?"

Winston had a sudden thought. "Syme will be vaporized! He is too intelligent. He thinks too clearly and the Party doesn't like that. One day he will disappear."

Syme looked across the canteen. "Here comes Parsons," he said.

Winston's neighbour at Victory House, a fat, middle-sized man with fair hair, was coming across the canteen.

"Hello," Parsons said, sitting down. As he sat down, Winston could smell his **sweat**. "Winston, old friend," he said. "I need some money from you. You forgot to give me your money for Hate Week. Victory House is going to have the largest number of flags in the whole street. I need $2.00 from you."

Winston felt in his pocket and pulled out two dirty dollar notes. He passed them across the table to Parsons. About a quarter of his salary had to be given away like this.

"By the way, old friend," said Parsons. "I hear that son of mine threw a stone at you yesterday. I told him he shouldn't do that again." Then he went on, proudly. "Guess what my little girl did last Saturday? She followed a strange man. She followed him for two hours, then she told a police patrol so they could arrest him."

"What did she do that for?" said Winston, rather surprised.

Parsons answered proudly, "She saw that his shoes looked odd so she knew he was probably a foreigner."

"What happened to him?" said Winston.

"Oh, I don't know, of course," replied Parsons. "But we are at war, so —" Parsons made the movements of firing a gun at someone.

Suddenly, a loud voice came from the telescreen. "Comrades," it announced excitedly, "We have great news for you! Our factories have made twenty percent more of everything this year. All over Oceania this morning, workers marched in the streets, thanking Big Brother for the happy life he has given us. They were also thanking him for raising the chocolate ration to twenty grams a week."

"Only yesterday," thought Winston, "the ration was reduced to twenty grams. How can people have forgotten that already? Am I the only person with a memory?"

Winston heard Parsons speaking to him. "Have you got any razor blades, old friend?"

"No, sorry," said Winston, but as he was speaking, he suddenly noticed something and felt very afraid.

The dark-haired young woman who had sat near him at the Daily Hate yesterday was sitting at the next table. She seemed to be looking carefully at him, and she looked away as soon as she saw him looking at her.

33

"Why is she watching me?" thought Winston. "Did she notice I didn't believe that the chocolate ration has been raised? Is she going to report me to the Thought Police for a facecrime?" You could be arrested if your face showed the wrong kind of thoughts.

Soon after, there was a loud whistle from the telescreen and they had to return to work.

CHAPTER FIVE
Two plus two make four

It was three years ago. It was on a dark evening, in a narrow street near one of the railway stations. She was standing under a street lamp that did not give much light. She had a young face, painted with very thick make-up so it looked like a **mask***. Party women never paint their faces. There was nobody else in the street, and no telescreen. She said, "It'll be $2.00." I –*

Winston was writing in his diary, but he stopped because it was too difficult to go on. From time to time, he had a terrible desire to **swear** as loudly as he could, or to hit his head against the wall or kick the table. He wanted to do any noisy or painful thing to prevent himself from remembering that time with the prole woman.

Having sex with a prole was an **offence** for Party members, but sometimes Winston – like many Party members – **risked** it. Then he would start to feel angry again. Now Winston hoped that writing about it might help. He breathed deeply and went on: *I went with her through a doorway in a wall and down some steps into a kitchen. There was a bed against a wall, and an oil lamp on a table, turned down very low. She –*

Thinking about that time made Winston think about his wife. He believed he was still married to Katherine because he had not heard that she was dead, and they had never been divorced. They had only been together for about fifteen months, ten or eleven years earlier, and they had parted when they found out that they could not have children. The Party believed that

35

sex was for having children, not for love or enjoyment. Boys and girls learned this from an early age, and a lot of them also joined the Anti-Sex Society, which was against having sex at all.

Winston remembered how Katherine was a tall, fair-haired young woman, with a handsome face. But, early in their married life, he had discovered that she was the stupidest person he had ever met. She understood nothing and talked in Party slogans. He could have carried on living with her if it had not been for one thing – sex. She wanted children, so she wanted to have sex, but she hated it. Winston had no desire for her and hated holding her stiff body. Then, at last, when no children came, they agreed to part.

Winston picked up his pen again and wrote: *The prole woman threw herself down on the bed, and at once pulled up her skirt. I –*

He saw himself standing in the dark kitchen, with the smell of dirt and the prole woman's cheap **perfume**.

"Why does it have to be like this?" he asked himself. "Why is it a thoughtcrime to want to love and be loved, and, more than that, to experience desire?"

But he had to write the rest of the story. He wrote how he had turned up the oil lamp to see the woman better. Under the thick make-up, her face was old and lined, and she had no teeth.

But I still went ahead and did it.

He put down his pen and closed his eyes. He had written it down at last, but it made no difference. He still wanted to swear as loudly as he could, but he said nothing. He picked up his pen again and wrote: *If there is hope, it is with the proles.*

"The proles are eighty-five percent of the population of

Oceania, so there are enough people to make an army and defeat the Party," he thought. "Party members can't destroy the Party – there aren't enough of them. The proles, if they realized how much strength they have, could get together and overthrow the Party."

But immediately Winston had another thought. "They won't. They don't realize what the real problems are. They just fight and swear and argue among themselves. He remembered feeling excited one day when he suddenly heard huge shouts and cries coming from a prole part of the city. *"It's started,"* he had thought. *"The proles are starting a **revolution** against the Party."* For a moment, he had heard the huge **power** of the proles. Then he had seen a large crowd of people in a market, where someone was selling pans, which were **rare** things in London. The noise was of people fighting over the pans. Two women near Winston were kicking each other. Winston had felt angry. He wrote: *Until they become **conscious**, the proles won't **rebel**; and until they have rebelled, they can't become conscious.*

Of course, the Party said it had saved the proles from the rich businessmen in the Great Revolution. The history textbooks of the Party explained how, before the Revolution, prole children had been forced to work in factories from the age of six. Women had been forced to work underground, digging for coal. In fact, everybody had awful lives – they were beaten and given no food. Women today still dug for coal underground and the Party taught that the proles were like animals who must be controlled by a few simple rules. It was, Winston realized, a perfect example of doublethink because the lives of the proles today were as bad

37

as they had been before the Revolution. The Party left them to be born, live, have children and die early deaths. There were a lot of criminals among the proles, but, because they only fought and stole from each other, the Party did not care. Most prole homes did not have telescreens. There was a Party slogan: *PROLES AND ANIMALS ARE FREE.*

The Party said that everybody was healthier, bigger, stronger, happier, more intelligent and better educated than people fifty years ago. But 'history' for the people of Oceania was always changing, so the stories of life before the Great Revolution could just as easily be false as true.

Then Winston remembered how, just once, a few years ago, he had held in his hands a piece of paper which proved that the past had been changed.

In the years after the Revolution, most of its leaders had been executed on the orders of Big Brother, after they had confessed to their crimes in long, public trials. In particular, three important Party members had been executed after they confessed to working for Eurasia. About five years after this, Winston had found a page of an old copy of the *Times*, which was with some instructions he had received. It included the date when the newspaper was published and had a photograph of the three men attending a Party meeting in New York. In the trial, they had confessed to being in Siberia on that day, selling secrets to the Eurasian army. So their confessions had been lies which they had been forced to make, maybe by being **tortured**.

Winston thought back to how he had felt when he had seen the photograph in the newspaper. It had felt so strange to hold the piece of paper in his hands. He had been afraid that the telescreen might show someone what he had found. Very quickly, he had put the page of newspaper with the photograph into a memory hole so that it would be burned. Now he thought, "Why does the Party make such a huge effort to rewrite history? What difference does it make?" The reason for doing it was a mystery to him. Picking up his pen again, he wrote: *I understand HOW; I do not understand WHY.*

He wondered now, as he had done many times before, whether he was mad. If he was the only person in the world to believe that the past could not be changed, then he must be mad. But it was not the thought of being mad which frightened him, it was the thought of being wrong.

"In the end," he thought, "the Party will announce that two and two make five, and you will have to believe it or be executed. And the most terrifying thing won't be that they kill you for disagreeing, but that the Party is right. For how do we know that two plus two make four? Or that the past cannot be changed?"

Then the face of O'Brien came into his mind and Winston felt sure that O'Brien was on his side. Winston knew in this moment that the Party was wrong and that he was right. He had to hold on to the truth, even about little things. He was writing the diary for O'Brien, speaking to O'Brien. He wrote: *Freedom is the freedom to say that two plus two make four. If that is allowed, then everything else follows.*

CHAPTER SIX
The shop

When Winston left work at the end of the next day, the weather was fine. Suddenly, he decided not to go to the **Community Centre** that evening, and to take a long walk instead. It was not a very good thing to do because people at the Community Centre would notice that he was not there and Party members were not supposed to do anything on their own. But today, Winston did not want a noisy evening at the Centre with boring games, talks and people being friendly because they had drunk too much Victory Gin. So, he started out on his walk, not caring where he went.

After a few kilometres, he went through a dirty, dusty prole area which was once called Saint Pancras. It was not an offence go to prole areas, but Party members did not usually visit them. A patrol might stop him and he would have to answer awkward questions: "What are you doing here, Comrade? What time did you leave work? Is this your usual way home?" But despite the danger he kept walking and, as he walked, he kept remembering the strange truth that he had written in his diary: *If there is hope, it is with the proles.*

As he walked along a dirty street, among crowds of proles, two women who were talking in a doorway stopped and stared at him as if he was an odd kind of animal. Suddenly, someone shouted, "Lie flat on the ground, Mister!" Quickly, Winston obeyed the instruction. A few moments later, a rocket bomb fell very close to him. He was covered with broken glass, but he was not hurt and he got up and continued walking. Further along the street, he saw the ruins of a group of houses where the bomb had struck. He turned down a narrow street and into a new area of the city.

It was nearly twenty hours, and the drinking shops, or pubs as the proles called them, were full. The noise of arguments and the smell of sweat came out of the open doors as Winston passed them. He heard some men arguing loudly.

"Listen to me," one of them was saying angrily. "I tell you no number ending in seven has won in more than a year."

"Yes, it has!" shouted one of the others.

They were talking about a competition to win money, which was the only Party event the proles cared about. However, all the Party members knew that the amazing weekly prizes did not exist. There were a few real prizes for 'lucky winners', enough to keep the proles interested.

"If there is hope, it is with the proles," Winston thought again, but when he looked at the uneducated, unthinking people around him, he knew that it was only a small hope.

Winston had a feeling he had been on this street before. Then he realized he was near the shop where he had bought the book which had become his diary. A feeling of fear went through him. He had promised himself he would not come near this place again. And yet, his feet had brought him back here. He noticed that although it was nearly twenty-one hours, the shop was still open. He went inside, thinking he could say he was trying to buy razor blades if anyone questioned him.

The owner had just lit an oil lamp, which had a warm, friendly smell. He was a man of about sixty, old and bent, with a long nose and gentle eyes behind thick glasses. His hair was almost white and he was wearing a black jacket made from old, but expensive cloth.

"I recognized you on the pavement," he said. "You're the gentleman who bought that book made from beautiful paper." He looked at Winston over the top of his glasses. "Do you want anything special?"

"I was just passing," said Winston. "I don't want anything in particular."

"That's a good thing," said the man, "because I don't suppose I have anything interesting." He waved his arm at the things in the shop. "It's hard to find things to sell these days. Anything metal is being melted down to make guns."

Winston looked around the tiny shop, which was in fact very full of old things, but none of them looked valuable. He wandered towards a small table where he noticed a round, smooth object that shone in the lamplight. It was a heavy piece of glass, round on one side, and flat on the other, like half of a ball. The colour reminded him of rainwater and in the middle of it, there was a strange pink object.

"What is it?" asked Winston, picking it up.

"It's a **paperweight** with **coral** inside it," said the old man. "It's more than a hundred years old. The coral comes from deep in the Indian Ocean."

"It's a beautiful thing," said Winston.

"There aren't many people who are interested in beautiful

things these days," said the old man. "If you wanted to buy it, it would be four dollars."

Winston immediately paid four dollars and put the paperweight into his pocket. The old man looked happier now that Winston had bought something. "There's another room upstairs which you might like to have a look at," the old man said. "There are just a few pieces in it."

He lit another lamp and led the way slowly up some narrow stairs and into a living room above the back of the shop, which had a view down to a backyard and across roofs. There was an old clock with a twelve-hour face on a shelf over the fireplace, carpet on the floor and some pictures on the walls. Under the window, there was an enormous wooden bed.

"My wife and I lived here till she died," said the old man. "I'm selling everything now." He was holding the lamp high so Winston could see the whole room. There was no telescreen. A thought went through Winston's mind – it would probably be quite easy to rent the room for a few dollars a week, if he **dared** to.

"Now, if you're interested in old pictures . . ." the old man said, holding up the lamp to show a picture on one side of the fireplace. Winston examined the picture, which showed an old building with a tower.

"The picture is fixed to the wall," said the old man, "but I could take it down for you, if you like."

"I recognize that building," said Winston. "It's a ruin now."

"That's right. Rocket bombs destroyed it many years ago," replied the old man. "It was a church – once it was called St Clement's Dane."

"I knew that it had been a church," Winston said.

Winston talked to the old man for a few more minutes and learned that his name was Charrington. He decided that in about a month he would come back and buy the picture of the church, take it out of its wooden **frame** and hide it under his jacket to take home.

Feeling a little frightened about what he had done and what he was thinking, Winston left the shop in a hurry. But as soon as he was outside, he saw someone wearing the blue overalls of the Party coming towards him. It was the dark-haired young woman from the Fiction Department. She looked straight at him, then hurried past. Winston had no doubt now that she must be spying on him. She must have followed him. Was she just spying on him because she wanted to? Or was she actually working for the Thought Police?

Winston was filled with terror and he felt a sharp pain in his stomach. At first, he could not make himself move. He thought about running after the woman and hitting her on the head with a stone from the street or even with the glass paperweight in his pocket. But he quickly realized that he could not run after her because she was younger and probably stronger than him. All he wanted to do was to get home, sit down and be quiet. Slowly, he began to walk.

It was after twenty-two hours when he got back to the flat. He went into the kitchen and drank a teacup of Victory Gin. Then he got out his diary, but he could not think what to write. He tried to think about the face of O'Brien, but that did not help. He tried to think about the place where there is no darkness that

O'Brien had spoken about in his dream, but instead, the face of Big Brother came into his mind. Winston pulled a coin out of his pocket and seeing Big Brother's calm smile, began to feel that there was no hope for a better future.

CHAPTER SEVEN
I love you

Four days after Winston had seen the dark-haired woman in the street, he saw her again. It was the middle of the morning and Winston was walking along a corridor in the Ministry. She was walking towards him and, as she came nearer, he noticed that her right arm had a bandage round it. When she was about four metres away from him, she suddenly fell over and gave a cry of pain. She must have fallen on her injured arm. Winston stopped. The woman got up on to her knees, looking at him as if asking for help. Winston felt strange – this was an enemy who was trying to kill him, but she was also a human being and she was in pain. He moved towards her.

"Are you hurt?" he asked.

"It's nothing. My arm. It'll be all right in a second," she said.

"Have you broken anything?"

"No, I'm all right. It just hurt for a moment."

She held out her hand to him, and he helped her up. She was starting to look better.

"It's nothing," she said. "Thanks, Comrade."

Then she walked on down the corridor as though it really had been nothing. The whole event had probably taken less than half a minute. Winston had learned not to show his feelings on his face, but it had been hard not to look surprised when, as he was helping her up, she had put something into his hand. It was a small piece of folded paper.

He went back to his cubicle and sat down, quickly pushing

the piece of paper into the collection of documents on his desk. Then he pulled his speakwrite towards him and started to work.

"I mustn't open the paper for at least five minutes," he told himself. His heart was beating fast as he bent over his work. "There are two possibilities," he thought. "It's a message from the Thought Police, though I don't know why they would deliver a message in such a strange way. Or perhaps it's from some kind of underground organization. Perhaps Goldstein's Brotherhood exists after all! Perhaps the woman belongs to it." So part of his mind told him that the message meant death, but another part of his mind felt hope.

Finally, Winston finished the piece of work he was doing. He put the papers into the tube. Eight minutes had passed. He pulled the next documents towards him, with the folded piece of paper among them. He unfolded it. There were three words on it: *I love you*.

For several seconds, he did not do anything. Although he knew it was dangerous to show any interest in anything, he quickly read the words again before he threw the piece of paper into the memory hole. For the rest of the morning, he found it very hard to work. At lunchtime, it was horrible to be in the noisy, crowded canteen. The afternoon was easier as he had a long, difficult piece of work which took several hours to complete, and for more than two hours he succeeded in forgetting about the woman. Then the memory of her face came back, and he just wanted to be alone so he could think about what had happened. That evening, he went to the Community Centre. He was bored, but for once he did not mind being there. The sight of the words 'I love you' had made him want to stay alive and not take stupid **risks**. Finally, at twenty-three hours, when he was in bed, away from the telescreen and safe in the darkness, he was able to think.

He knew now that the woman was not his enemy. He knew that she had been afraid when she handed him the note. Only five nights ago he had thought about hitting her on the head with a stone, but now he thought of her young, naked, beautiful body, as he had seen it in his dream about the Golden Country. He was afraid that she would change her mind if he did not get in touch with her quickly. He decided that the safest place to meet her was the canteen. If she sat at a table by herself, somewhere in the middle of the room, not too near the telescreens and with conversation going on all around, he could sit there, too. Then they would be able to talk for a very short time.

For a week after this, his life was like a bad dream. On the next day, she did not come to the canteen until he was leaving it. On the day after that, she was in the canteen, but with three other young women. Then, for three awful days she did not appear at all. What had happened to her? She might have been vaporized. She might have been sent to the other end of Oceania. Worst of all, he was worried that she might have changed her mind. He did not sleep properly and the only way he could escape from his worry was by working.

The next day, Winston arrived at the canteen early. The woman was sitting at a table on her own, away from the telescreens. Winston carried his tray to her table, sat down opposite her and started eating. They did not look at each other. Then, while they were eating, they had a very short conversation.

"What time do you leave work?" he whispered.

"Eighteen-thirty," she replied quietly.

"Where can we meet?"

"Victory Square, near the **monument**."

"There are lots of telescreens."

"It doesn't matter if there's a crowd of people," she said. "Don't come up to me until you see me among a lot of people. And don't look at me."

"What time?"

"Nineteen hours."

"All right."

She finished her lunch quickly and left, while Winston continued eating.

Winston arrived early that evening in Victory Square. He walked among the crowds of people near the tall monument with its statue of Big Brother at the top. At five minutes past nineteen hours, the woman still had not appeared. Winston felt afraid. She was not coming! She had changed her mind! Then suddenly there was shouting and the noise of heavy trucks. People began to run towards a road and the young woman ran past him with them. Winston followed her. He pushed through the crowd and stood next to her as they watched a long line of trucks full of Eurasian prisoners going past them. The woman's cheek was close enough for him to feel its warmth. Her shoulder and her arm were pressed against his. She took control as she had done in the canteen.

"Can you hear me?" she whispered.

"Yes."

"Can you get Sunday afternoon off work?"

"Yes."

"Then listen carefully. You'll have to remember this. Go to Paddington Station –"

She gave Winston instructions about how to get to the place where they should meet, including a half-hour journey by train, a walk along a road, through a gate, on to a path, past a dead tree and into some woods. It was as if she had a map in her head. "Can you remember all that?" she asked finally.

"Yes. What time?"

"About fifteen. You may have to wait. I'll come a different way. Are you sure you can remember everything?"

"Yes."

"Then get away from me as quickly as you can."

But, for the moment, they could not get out of the thick crowd. The trucks were still going past and the people were watching quietly. The only foreigners they ever saw, whether Eurasian or Eastasian, were prisoners, who were like strange animals to them. As Winston stood beside the woman, looking not at her, but at the prisoners, she took hold of his hand. He felt her hand, touching her fingers, her nails and her wrist. Although he only held it for a few seconds, Winston felt sure he would recognize it if he saw it.

CHAPTER EIGHT
Julia

On Sunday afternoon Winston was a bit early. The train journey had been easy and he had quickly found the path which the woman had told him about. It was 2nd May and the sun was shining. Winston walked into a wood where the sun shone down through the trees. He had no watch, but he knew that it could not be fifteen hours yet. He heard a sound behind him and he felt afraid. Had someone followed him? Then he felt a hand on his shoulder and looked round. It was the woman. She shook her head, telling him to keep quiet, then quickly led him further into the wood. There were no telescreens, but there could be hidden **microphones**.

The warm sunshine made Winston feel dirty and old. He felt sure that if she turned round and looked at him, she would decide that she did not want to be there. The woman pushed past some branches into a small open space which had tall young trees around it. She stopped and turned. Winston stopped too – he felt afraid to go closer to her.

"Here we are," she said. "I didn't want to say anything on the path in case there was a microphone. We'll be all right here – no one can see because of the trees and there's nowhere to hide a microphone."

Winston moved closer to her. She was smiling at him.

"Your eyes are light brown," he said. "I didn't know what colour they were until now. But now that you've seen what I'm really like, can you still look at me?"

"Yes, easily," she said.

"I'm thirty-nine years old. I've got a wife I can't get divorced from. I'm not very healthy. My back hurts and I've got a terrible cough."

"I don't care," she replied.

The next moment, she was in his arms. He felt amazed. He could feel her hair against his face and he was kissing her wide red mouth. She called him "darling" and "loved one", and when he pulled her on to the ground, she fell there happily. They could have had sex then, but Winston did not feel able to. He was glad this was happening, but it was too soon.

"There's no hurry," she said. "We've got the whole afternoon." She sat against him, putting her arm around his waist. "This is a great place, isn't it? I found it when I was out on a community walk."

"What's your name?" asked Winston.

"Julia. I know yours. It's Winston – Winston Smith."

"How did you find that out?"

"Oh, I'm good at finding things out," she said. "Tell me, what did you think of me before that day I gave you the note?"

Winston did not feel that he had to lie to her. "I hated you," he said. "I wanted to kill you – I wanted to hit you on the head with a stone. I imagined you were something to do with the Thought Police."

She laughed. "You thought I was a good Party member, enjoying banners and slogans and games and community walks, didn't you? And you thought I'd denounce you as a thought-criminal so you would be executed."

"Yes, I did," replied Winston. "A lot of young women are like that."

Julia pulled off the red scarf of the Anti-Sex Society. "You thought that because I was wearing this thing," she said, and threw it away. Then she felt in the pocket of her overalls and found a small bar of chocolate. She broke it and gave half to Winston.

"I bought it on the **black market**," she said. "People steal things like chocolate and sell them all the time, but I *am* a good Party member. I have to be because it's the only way to be safe."

Winston ate the chocolate, which was dark and shiny and very different from the normal soft brown stuff that had a horrible taste. The taste reminded him of something bad he had done in the past; something that he would have liked to put right, but could not.

"You're ten or fifteen years younger than me," he said. "What could you see in a man like me?"

"It was something in your face. I'm good at noticing people who don't belong anywhere. As soon as I saw you, I knew you were against *them*."

When Julia said *them*, Winston knew she meant the Party. She talked so openly about the Party, with such a huge amount of hate, it made Winston feel nervous, even though he knew they must be safe here. As they talked, they left the circle of trees and walked through the wood with their arms around each other's waists. At the edge of the wood, they looked out into the fields and Winston was shocked to recognize the view.

"Is there a narrow river somewhere near here?" he asked. He spoke quietly because they were **no longer** hidden in the trees.

"Yes, it's at the edge of the next field," she said.

"It's the Golden Country," he whispered.

"What's the Golden Country?"

"It's somewhere I've sometimes seen in a dream," he replied.

"Listen!" whispered Julia.

A small bird was sitting on a branch quite close to them, singing. In the quiet afternoon, its beautiful song was very loud. The music went on and on, and Winston and Julia held each other. She felt soft and warm in his arms. Winston put his lips against her ear.

"Now," he said.

"Not here," she said. "Come back to where we were. It's safer."

When they were back in the circle of trees, Julia turned to face Winston, smiling. Quickly, she took off her Party overalls and then the rest of her clothes, as she had in his dream. She stood smiling in front of him.

"Have you done this before?" he asked.

"Of course – lots of times."

"With Party members?"

"Yes, but not with Inner Party members, of course. And I love it."

This was what Winston wanted to hear. When they had sex, it would be because they loved each other and because they would enjoy it. They were fighting against the Party. This desire for sex was the force that would tear the Party to pieces. He pulled her gently down on to the grass.

They fell asleep together afterwards, and when they woke, Julia took control. She told him a different way to go home and said she would leave first. She told him where they could meet again, in four days' time, near a busy market in a poor area of the city.

"And now I must go," she said. "I've got an Anti-Sex Society meeting at nineteen-thirty." She kissed him, almost violently. "Goodbye, my love," she said, then she pushed through the trees and disappeared.

———

During the rest of May, Winston and Julia only managed to make love once, in a ruined church, in another part of the countryside outside London. Often, they met for a few minutes in the streets after work, walking close but never together, and parting as soon as a police patrol came into view or a helicopter flew over. When they finally met in the church, they sat in a hot, dusty room in the tower and talked for hours. Winston told Julia about his marriage to Katherine. Julia told Winston that she was twenty-six and lived in a house with thirty other young women. She told him about a relationship she had had years ago with a Party member of sixty. "It was fortunate that he killed himself before the Thought Police could torture him and learn my name," she said.

Winston began to understand that Julia hated the Party because her aim in life was to have a good time, and the Party's aim was to stop her. She was not interested in politics and what INGSOC believed. She thought that **conspiracies** against the Party were stupid and useless, because it was impossible for them to succeed. Winston asked what she knew about Goldstein and the Brotherhood, and their conspiracy to overthrow the Party. But she did not believe the Brotherhood existed.

However, Julia understood something which Winston had never understood. She understood why it was important for the Party to prevent the enjoyment of sex.

"When you have sex, you're happy and in a world of your own – and the Party can't control you then," she said. "If you're happy inside yourself, why would you care about Big Brother and the Two-Minutes Hate and all their other stupid ideas? Also, if you only allow sex for making children, people get angry. The Party knows that and can turn that bad energy into hate."

Winston and Julia both believed that sooner or later, the Thought Police would catch them and they would be killed. But Julia was not as pessimistic as Winston, who knew that one person could never win and could never be happy. The only victory would be in the distant future, after they were dead, when the Party was defeated. Julia thought that happiness was possible if you were clever and lucky, and did not get caught.

"We are the dead," Winston said.

"We're not dead yet," replied Julia. Then she picked up a small piece of wood and began to draw a map on the dusty floor to show Winston the way to their next meeting place.

CHAPTER NINE

A love song and a rat

It was evening, the June sun was still high in the sky, and Winston was standing in the little room above Mr Charrington's shop. The bed had pillows and blankets on it. The old clock with the twelve-hour face was ticking on the shelf above the fireplace, and Winston's glass paperweight, in a corner on a little table, was shining in the sunlight. In front of the fireplace, a pan of water was on an old **stove** which Mr Charrington had provided. Winston had brought an envelope filled with Victory Coffee with him. The clock's hands said seven-twenty, but it was nineteen-twenty really. Julia was coming at nineteen-thirty.

While Winston was waiting for Julia he watched a fat prole woman singing a popular love song and hanging washing in the backyard. It was a song the proles had been singing for weeks. The words were romantic and stupid, probably written by a machine in the Music Department at the Ministry of Truth. But the woman had a beautiful, deep voice and the song sounded quite lovely.

Winston had rented the room from Mr Charrington, who seemed pleased to earn a few dollars and unsurprised that Winston was going to bring a woman to it. But Winston knew he was taking a big risk. It was an offence for Party members to have relationships with each other, and they would be punished if they were caught. They had not been able to meet for a number of weeks because of the preparations for Hate Week. When he explained the idea of meeting in the room above the shop, Julia had agreed at once, but they both knew what a crazy thing it was to do.

"We've taken another step towards our deaths in the Ministry of Love," Winston thought as he sat on the bed to wait for her.

At that moment, Julia ran into the room carrying a tool bag which she opened at once.

"Look what I've brought," she said. "If you've brought some of that horrible Victory Coffee, you can throw it away."

She sat on the floor and pulled the tools out of the bag. Underneath them were some paper packets. The first packet she gave to Winston felt as if it was full of sand. He thought he recognized how it felt and asked, "Is it sugar?"

"Yes, real sugar. And I've got some white bread and a little jar of jam, and a tin of milk. But look at this . . ." She began to remove some cloth from around a packet. "I had to wrap it up because of the smell."

The rich smell was filling the room. Winston knew it from when he was a child. "It's real coffee," he said.

"It's all Inner Party stuff," said Julia, "but of course, it's easy to buy things on the black market. Now, sit on the bed with your back to me and don't turn round till I tell you to."

As Winston waited, he could still hear the prole woman singing in the backyard.

"You can turn round now," said Julia.

For a second, Winston did not recognize her. She had painted her face like a prole woman. Her lips and her cheeks were red.

She looked much prettier and like a woman. This was the first time that he had ever seen a female Party member with make-up on. He took her in his arms.

"And you've got perfume as well?" he asked.

"Yes," she replied. "Next I'm going to get a dress and some nice shoes. In this room, I'm going to be a woman, not a Party member."

They took off their clothes quickly, fell on to the big bed together and made love. Double beds were rare and Julia had never been in one before.

After a while, they fell asleep for a short time. The clock's hands showed nine o'clock when Winston woke up. He did not move, because Julia was sleeping with her head on his arm. He looked at her beautiful face, a little red make-up still on her cheek. The evening sun shone gently on the end of the bed. He wondered whether in the past it was normal for a man and a woman to lie in bed with no clothes on, making love when they wanted to and saying whatever they wanted to each other. Was there ever a time when it was ordinary to do this?

Julia woke up. "I'll get up and make some coffee in a moment," she said. Then suddenly she shouted, "Hi, get out, you dirty animal!" She picked up a shoe from beside the bed and threw it across the room.

"What was it?" asked Winston in surprise.

"A rat," she replied. "I saw his horrible nose. There's a hole over there."

"Rats," said Winston quietly. "In this room."

"They're everywhere," said Julia. She did not sound worried.

"Did you know they attack children? People won't leave their babies alone. It's the big brown rats that are the worst. They . . ."

"Stop! Don't go on!" said Winston, his eyes tightly shut.

"What's the matter? You've gone so pale," said Julia.

"Rats – the most horrible things in the world," he whispered, his eyes still shut.

Julia put her arms around him and held him close to her. For a few moments, Winston kept his eyes closed. He was back in a horrible dream, standing in front of a wall of darkness, knowing there was something terrifying on the other side.

"I'm sorry," he said at last. "It's nothing. I hate rats, that's all."

"Don't worry," she said. "I'll put something in the hole before we go, so they can't get in again."

Julia got out of bed, pulled on her overalls and made the coffee. The smell from the pan was so strong that they closed the window in case anyone outside smelled it. What made the coffee even better was the sugar, which made it smooth in a way Winston had almost forgotten. As she drank her coffee and ate bread and jam, Julia walked around the room. She stopped in front of the picture of the church. "What's this place?" she asked. "I've seen it before."

"It was a church called St Clement's Dane," Winston replied.

"That picture is really dirty," said Julia. "I'll take it down one day and clean it. I suppose it's time we left. I'll wash this make-up off. Then I'll get it off your face as well!"

Winston lay on the bed a bit longer. It was getting dark now and he lay on his side looking into the glass paperweight. He had the feeling that he and Julia were inside it, with the bed and the clock and the picture and the paperweight itself. The paperweight was the room they were in and the coral was Julia's life and his own, fixed in its centre.

CHAPTER TEN
O'Brien

Syme had disappeared. One day, some people noticed that he was not at work. But the next day, nobody mentioned him. On the third day, Winston went to look for his friend's name on a noticeboard. There were lists on it of the members of clubs and societies, and one of the clubs was the Chess Club. Syme had been a member, but his name was not on the list. Nothing had been crossed out – the list was just one name shorter. Syme did not exist. He had never existed.

The weather was burning hot during June and everyone was working very hard preparing for Hate Week, especially Winston's neighbour Parsons. He took control of all the flags, banners and posters on Victory House because he was trying to make sure it had more than any other building in London. A new Hate Song had been written. All day, the telescreens played it, the proles shouted it in the streets, and in Victory House, the two Parsons children sang it all the time. A huge poster of a Eurasian soldier had appeared on lots of walls. The soldier was carrying a gun and when people were near the poster, the gun was always pointing at them. Adding to the mood of hate, more rocket bombs landed on the city, killing larger numbers of people than usual, including a lot of children in a school playground.

Winston and Julia met seven times at the room above the shop during June. Winston had stopped drinking Victory Gin. He was fatter and healthier and he no longer coughed in the mornings. Life was no longer so hard. Both of them knew that what was happening could not last long. Sometimes when they lay in bed together they held each other very tightly as if it was the last time they would ever do it. But there were other times when they felt safe. It was as if they were inside Winston's paperweight, where no harm could come to them.

Often they talked of escaping. They would become proles, get jobs in a factory and live their whole lives together in a place where nobody would find them. Katherine would die and they would get married.

However, they never agreed about fighting the power of the Party. Julia was uninterested in politics, although in some ways she understood things better than Winston. She thought that the Party arranged for the rocket bombs to fall on London regularly in order to make people frightened all the time. She did not believe there was really a war at all, an idea which Winston had never thought about before.

Julia did not care whether what she was told was the truth or lies. For example, when Winston explained that the Party did not invent aeroplanes, as they had learned at school, because planes had existed before he was born, she was not interested. It frightened Winston a bit that she did not remember what happened in the recent past. It meant that she could not see the lies they were being told today. When he told her about his work at the Records Department, writing lies to change newspaper reports, she was not shocked. "Who cares?" was all she said.

Winston tried to make Julia understand what the Party was doing. He told her about finding the photograph of the three important Party members who had been executed after they confessed to working for Eurasia. She listened as he told her how he had found the photograph in an old copy of the *Times*. He explained how this proved the three men had been in New York on the day they had confessed that they were in Siberia selling secrets to the Eurasians.

"History has stopped," Winston said. "The Party has made an endless present and what they say and do is always right. If I had had the courage to keep that piece of paper, I could have shown it to a few people. And they might have started to doubt the Party. I don't think we can change anything during our lives, but maybe the next **generations** could continue what we started."

But Julia did not care about that either.

"I'm not interested in the next generation," she said. "I'm interested in us."

"You're only a **rebel** from the waist downwards," Winston told her.

Julia thought this was very funny and threw her arms around him, laughing.

———

It happened at last. Winston was walking down a corridor in the Ministry of Truth when he felt that someone was walking behind him. The person coughed as if he was about to speak. Winston stopped and turned round. It was O'Brien. Winston's heart jumped violently. He realized that he could not speak. But O'Brien put a friendly hand on Winston's arm for a moment, so

Winston turned again and they began walking together side by side. O'Brien began to speak in the serious, slow voice that all the Inner Party members used.

"I've been hoping to talk to you," he said. "I was reading one of your Newspeak articles in the *Times* the other day. You're very interested in Newspeak, I believe?"

"I'm interested in it, but I've never had anything to do with writing the dictionary," Winston managed to reply.

"But you write it very elegantly," said O'Brien. "This is not just my own opinion. I was talking to a friend of yours recently who is an expert. I can't remember his name for the moment."

Winston's heart jumped again. O'Brien must mean Syme. But Syme was dead, and he was not only dead, he was an unperson. O'Brien had shared a thoughtcrime with Winston when he mentioned him. This must be a sign to show him that he and O'Brien were joined together in some way.

O'Brien went on. "I noticed you had used two words in your article which are no longer in the dictionary. Have you seen the tenth edition of the Newspeak Dictionary?"

"No," replied Winston. "We're still using the ninth edition in the Records Department."

"There are a few copies of the tenth edition available. In fact, I have one myself," said O'Brien. "Perhaps you would like to look at it?"

"Yes, very much," replied Winston, immediately understanding what O'Brien was going to do.

"Good. Perhaps you could collect it from my flat," said O'Brien. "Let me give you the address."

O'Brien wrote his address on a small piece of paper with a gold pen. He gave the paper to Winston saying, "I am usually at home in the evenings."

Then he was gone. Winston read the address and later dropped the piece of paper into a memory hole. Their meeting had only lasted for about two minutes. Winston decided that it could only have one meaning. A conspiracy against the Party existed and O'Brien was inviting him to join it.

"My first step towards this day was my first secret thought," Winston said to himself. "My second step was when I moved from thoughts to words and started writing my diary. Now I'm going to move from words to actions when I go to visit O'Brien. And the last step will happen in the Ministry of Love. I know it and accept it. But I feel like I'm stepping into my grave."

CHAPTER ELEVEN
The proles are human beings

In the room above Mr Charrington's shop, Winston woke up beside Julia with his eyes full of tears. He had dreamed about his mother and sister, and the dream had taken place in the bright world inside the glass paperweight. The glass top of the paperweight had become the sky. And while he was inside the paperweight, he had been able to see his life clearly. He had remembered the last time he saw his mother, and now he was awake, memories of what happened before she disappeared came back to him.

When his father disappeared, his mother did not show any surprise or any sadness, but she changed suddenly. She lost interest in everything. It seemed to Winston that she was waiting for something that she expected to happen. She did what was needed – cooking, washing, making the bed, cleaning the floor – very slowly. For hours at a time, she would sit very still on the bed holding his young sister, a small silent child who was two or three years old. Sometimes his mother would hold him very tightly in her arms for a long time without speaking.

More than anything else, he remembered the arguments at mealtimes. He was always hungry. He would ask again and again why there was not more food. He would shout at his mother, and she always gave him more than his share. During every meal she would ask him not to be selfish and to remember that his little sister was ill and needed food, but it was no use.

One day, they were given a bar of chocolate. It was a small bar for all three of them. It was obvious that it ought to be divided into three equal parts. Suddenly, Winston could hear his voice shouting that he should have the whole bar. His mother told him not to be greedy. There was a long argument, and in the end his mother gave three-quarters of the chocolate to Winston, and the other quarter to his sister. Winston stood watching his sister, who was in his mother's arms as usual. Then suddenly he took the chocolate out of his sister's hand and ran out of the door.

"Winston, Winston!" his mother shouted. "Come back! Give your sister back her chocolate!"

He stopped and turned, but he did not come back. His sister started crying quietly and, as his mother held the little girl more tightly, Winston suddenly realized that his sister was dying. He turned and ran downstairs. He never saw his mother again.

When he came back, his mother had disappeared. This was already becoming normal at that time. Nothing was gone from the room except his mother and his sister. To this day, he did not know whether or not his mother was dead. But now at last he had remembered that he was not responsible for her death.

He told Julia about the chocolate and his mother disappearing. Without opening her eyes, she said sleepily, "I expect you were a horrible child. All children are horrible."

"Yes. But the real point of the story is . . ."

Winston could tell from Julia's breathing that she was going to sleep. He continued to think about his mother. He thought about her holding his dying sister more tightly. She could not stop the child dying, but she could still love her. She felt that if you loved people, you just loved them, and when there was nothing else you could do, you still gave love. No power outside her could change that. The Party had done two terrible things. It had persuaded people that feelings, like love, did not matter, and it had taken away people's power over their own world. Two generations ago, people had cared about each other, whatever happened. Now the Party had power over everything people felt or did.

But the proles, he realized, were different. They had remained like the people of his mother's generation. They did not care about a Party or a country or an idea, they cared about each other. The proles had stayed human.

"The proles are human beings," he said aloud. "Those of us in the Party are not human."

These thoughts continued to worry him, and when Julia woke up again, he said, "Have you ever thought that the best thing for us to do would be to walk out of here before it's too late, and never see each other again?"

"Yes, several times," said Julia. "But I'm not going to do it."

"If we continue our relationship, we will be caught," he said. "We've been lucky, but our luck can't last much longer. We may be together for another six months or a year – we don't know. But, in the end, we are certain to be apart. Do you realize how alone we shall be? When they get hold of us, there will be nothing either of us can do for the other. If I confess, they'll shoot you, and if I refuse to confess, they'll shoot you just the same. Neither of us will know whether the other is alive or dead. The one thing that matters is that we shouldn't **betray** each other, although even that can't make any difference to what happens to us."

"Everybody always confesses," said Julia. "You can't help it. They torture you."

"I don't mean confessing. Confessing is not betraying someone. What we say or do doesn't matter – only feelings matter. If they could make me stop loving you – that would be the real **betrayal**."

She thought about it. "They can't do that," she said. "They can make you say anything, but they can't make you believe it. They can't get inside you."

"I agree," he said. "They can't get inside you. If you can feel that staying human is a good thing, even if that doesn't change anything, you've beaten them."

CHAPTER TWELVE
The Brotherhood

They had done it; they were there at last.

Winston and Julia were standing in a long, elegant living room. At the far end of the room O'Brien was sitting at a table with lots of documents next to him. He had not looked up when the **servant** had brought Winston and Julia into the room.

Winston's heart was beating so hard that he wondered if he would be able to speak. It had been such a dangerous thing to do. He had met Julia outside O'Brien's door, and he had been scared the whole way there. He had been especially scared when he entered the area where the Inner Party members lived. A guard with a gun might stop him and tell him to get away.

The building was very large. It had clean, white-painted corridors, there were smells of good food and there were quick, silent lifts. Everything was so different from the places where Outer Party members lived.

O'Brien had his head bent over a piece of paper, looking powerful and intelligent. He spoke sharply in Newspeak into the speakwrite, then at last he stood up and came towards them across the soft, expensive carpet. As O'Brien passed the telescreen, he pressed a button on the wall. The voice stopped. Julia made a tiny sound of surprise. Even though he was so afraid, Winston could not help speaking.

"You can turn it off!" he said.

"Yes," said O'Brien, "we are allowed to turn it off."

He was opposite them now. He was much taller and more powerful than both of them. Obviously, he was waiting for Winston to speak. The room was completely silent without the sound of the telescreen. Suddenly, O'Brien started to smile.

"Shall I speak or will you?" he said.

"I will," said Winston quickly. "Is the telescreen really turned off?"

"Yes, everything is turned off. We are alone."

"We're here because —" Winston was uncertain what to say, but then he continued. "We believe that there's an organization working against the Party, and a conspiracy, and that you're involved in it. We want to join it. We're enemies of the Party. We don't believe in the ideas of INGSOC. We're thought-criminals. We're also having a relationship. I'm telling you this because we want to help you."

Winston stopped speaking because the door opened and the servant came in carrying a tray with glasses and a bottle on it. O'Brien filled up the glasses with the dark-red liquid. Julia picked up her glass and held it near her nose. The liquid had a slightly sweet smell.

"It's called wine," said O'Brien, smiling. "You have read about it in books, no doubt. Outer Party members don't see much of it, I'm afraid." He raised his glass. "Let us drink to the health of our leader, Goldstein."

Winston and Julia drank the wine, and then Winston asked, "So Goldstein exists?"

"Yes, he exists, but I don't know where he is," replied O'Brien.

"And is the organization called the Brotherhood real?" asked Winston. "And is the conspiracy real or did the Thought Police invent it?"

"Yes, the Brotherhood is real and so is the conspiracy," said O'Brien. "Now, I need to ask you some questions. First, what are you prepared to do?"

"We'll do anything that we're able to," said Winston.

O'Brien turned in his chair so that he was looking at Winston. He seemed to believe that Winston could speak for Julia.

"Are you prepared to die?"

"Yes."

"Are you prepared to do things which may cause the death of hundreds of innocent men, women and children?"

"Yes."

"Are you prepared to kill yourselves, if you are ordered to do so?"

"Yes."

"Are you prepared, the two of you, to separate and never see each other again?"

"No!" said Julia.

There was a short pause. Winston was not sure what he was going to say until he spoke.

"No," he said.

"Thank you for telling me," said O'Brien. "It is necessary for us to know everything. Now, you must understand something. You will belong to the Brotherhood, but you will never know much about it. You will only know a few people who will give you orders, and you will obey the orders without knowing why.

You will be caught. When you are finally caught, you will confess, but you won't have much to confess. You will only betray a few people. Probably you won't even betray me. By that time I may be dead, or I shall have become a different person."

As O'Brien continued to speak, Winston realized how much he admired this big, powerful man. Julia looked as if she admired O'Brien, too, as he explained the future. "You will have to get used to living without results and without hope. You will work for a while, you will be caught, you will confess and then you will die. There is no chance of much change during our lives. We can only spread our ideas from person to person and from generation to generation so the future is better than our present. In the fight against the Thought Police, there is no other way."

He looked at his watch. "It's almost time for you to go, Comrades," he said. "You mustn't leave together. You must go first," he said to Julia. "And take one of these." He gave her a flat white pill from a box which he took from a shelf. "It is important not to go out smelling of wine."

As soon as Julia had left, he turned to Winston. "Have you got a hiding place?" he asked.

Winston explained about the room above Mr Charrington's shop.

"Good," replied O'Brien. "Though it will often be necessary to change hiding places. Meanwhile I shall send you a copy of a book by Goldstein as soon as possible."

They were silent for a moment.

"If we meet again –" said O'Brien.

Winston completed the sentence: "– it will be in the place where there is no darkness."

O'Brien nodded as if he was not surprised to hear Winston complete the sentence. "And now," he said, "I'm afraid it is time for you to go. Let me give you one of these pills."

CHAPTER THIRTEEN
The book

Hate Week was noisy and busy. There were speeches, shouting, singing, banners and posters. Crowds marched through London, planes flew across the sky, military trucks drove down the streets and there was the sound of guns. After six days, the crowds hated Eurasia so much that they would have killed any Eurasian prisoners they saw. But suddenly it was announced during a speech in Victory Square that Eastasia, and not Eurasia, was the enemy.

Winston was in the square at the moment it was announced. The crowd was listening to a small thin man from the Inner Party shouting about the **torture** of Oceanian prisoners and the bombing of the people of Oceania by their Eurasian enemies. As he spoke, the crowd became more and more angry. Everybody was shouting, and the angriest shouts of all came from the schoolchildren. About twenty minutes after the speech had started, somebody hurried on to the platform and gave a piece of paper to the speaker. He read it without pausing in his speech and his voice did not change at all, but suddenly the names were different. Although he did not explain anything, the crowd understood. Oceania was at war with Eastasia!

At once, people started pulling down the posters which had the wrong faces on them. The schoolchildren, wearing the uniforms of the Spies, climbed on buildings and across roofs to untie banners. While they did this, the small man continued with his speech, and in a few minutes, everything had changed around him. Hate Week continued against a different enemy.

While people were tearing down the posters, a man whose face Winston did not see touched him on the shoulder and said, "Excuse me, I think you've dropped your case." Winston took the small case, without speaking. He knew that inside it was the book by Goldstein. He also knew that it would be many days before he would have time to look at it.

The speech did not finish until twenty-three hours, but afterwards Winston went straight to the Ministry of Truth, along with everybody else who worked there. They all knew what they had to do. They now believed that Oceania had always been at war with Eastasia. This meant that all the newspapers, photographs, films, books and other records of the past five years had to be changed. Everyone knew that at the end of one week there must be no record of the war with Eurasia.

Everyone in the Records Department worked eighteen hours a day, with two three-hour breaks to sleep. Everyone slept in the corridors, ate sandwiches and drank Victory Coffee. Every time Winston had finished with all the papers on his desk, new ones came out of the large tube.

By the third day, Winston had a headache and his eyes were very sore. He did not really remember that every word he said into the speakwrite and everything he wrote was a lie. Like everyone in the Records Department, he wanted to make the changes perfect. On the morning of the sixth day, the number of papers coming from the tube slowed down. Then there was nothing. The work was finished. It was now impossible for anyone to prove that Oceania had ever been at war with Eurasia.

At twelve hours, it was announced that all workers in the Ministry were free till the next morning. Winston, carrying the case containing Goldstein's book, went back to Victory House, shaved, and went straight out to Mr Charrington's shop.

When he climbed the stairs to their room, he felt tired, but not sleepy. He opened the window, lit the stove and put a pan of water on it so they could make coffee. Julia would arrive soon. Meanwhile he could start to read Goldstein's book. He had just turned to Chapter One when he heard Julia's footsteps on the stairs. She ran into his arms. It was more than a week since they had seen each other.

"I've got the book," he said.

"Oh, you've got it. Good," she said, without much interest. Then she bent down beside the stove to make the coffee.

Half an hour later, when they were lying in bed together, with the usual sound of the prole woman singing outside, Winston reached for the book and sat up.

"We must read it," he said. "All members of the Brotherhood have to read it."

Julia seemed to be about to fall asleep. "You read it," she said with her eyes shut. "Read it aloud. Then you can explain it to me while you're reading it."

Winston started reading. After a long time, he reached a chapter on the central importance of doublethink for Party members. "*Doublethink means believing two opposite truths at the same time, and accepting both of them.*" He realized that he was not learning anything new. He repeated aloud what he had once written in his diary: "*I understand HOW; I do not understand WHY.*"

However, he knew that the book came from a mind that was similar to his own, but one which was more powerful and less afraid to act.

He also realized that Julia was now asleep beside him. He shut the book, put it carefully on the floor, lay down and pulled a blanket over both of them. He shut his eyes. He could feel the sun on his face and Julia's smooth naked body touching his own. He felt strong, confident and safe. Everything was all right.

CHAPTER FOURTEEN
The Thought Police

When Winston woke, he felt as though he had slept for a long time. But when he looked at the old-fashioned clock, he saw that it was only half-past eight – twenty-thirty hours. He lay quietly for a while. Then the beautiful voice of the prole woman started again. The singing woke Julia and she got out of bed.

"I'm hungry," she said. "Let's make some more coffee. Oh! The stove has gone out – there's no oil in it."

"We can get some more from old Charrington, I expect," said Winston.

"But it's odd," said Julia. "I put plenty of oil in the stove. Anyway, I must put my clothes on. It's got colder."

Winston walked across to the window. The sun must have gone down behind the houses because it was not shining into the backyard any more. The prole woman walked backwards and forwards, hanging out her washing and singing. She was a big, fat woman of about fifty, but to Winston she looked beautiful in some way. She must have once been a pretty young woman like Julia, but after years of having children and working hard to look after them, she had grown to look like this. People like her all over the world would one day defeat the Party. *If there is hope, it is with the proles!* Without having read to the end of the book, he knew that must be Goldstein's final message.

"Do you remember," he said, "the bird that sang to us that first day?"

"He wasn't singing to us," said Julia. "He was just singing."

The birds sang, the proles sang, but the Party did not sing. The future belonged to the proles. They worked hard from birth to death, but they still sang.

"We are the dead," Winston said.

"We are the dead," Julia repeated.

"You are the dead," said a hard voice behind them.

Winston felt his body turn to ice. Julia's face turned white.

"You are the dead," repeated the voice.

"It was behind the picture," whispered Julia.

"It was behind the picture," said the voice. "Stay where you are. Do not move until you are told to do so."

They could do nothing except stand looking at each other. There was a loud noise above the fireplace and the sound of breaking glass. The picture fell to the floor, revealing a telescreen behind it.

"Now they can see us," said Julia.

"Now we can see you," said the voice. "Stand back to back. Put your hands behind your heads. Do not touch each other."

As they stood back to back, it seemed to Winston that he could feel Julia's body shaking. Or maybe it was just his own body shaking. The woman's singing stopped, there were angry shouts and the sound of something being thrown across the backyard. Then there was a cry of pain.

"There are people all round the house," said Winston.

"There are people all round the house," said the voice.

"I suppose we should say goodbye," said Julia.

"You should say goodbye," said the voice.

Behind Winston's back, broken glass landed on the bed. The top of a ladder had come through the window. Someone was climbing through the broken wooden frame. There was the sound of heavy footsteps on the stairs. Then the room was full of men in black uniforms, wearing big boots and carrying long black **truncheons**. There was another loud noise. Someone had picked up the glass paperweight from the table and thrown it on to the floor, where it broke into pieces. Winston saw a small piece of coral lying near him. "How small it is!" he thought. "How small it always was!"

There was a cry behind him. One of the men had hit Julia in her stomach with his truncheon. She was on the floor, trying to breathe. Winston did not dare turn his head, but he could see her white face, showing her pain. Then two of the men picked her up by her knees and shoulders and carried her out of the room. That was the last Winston saw of her.

No one had hit Winston yet. He wondered whether the men had got Mr Charrington. He wondered what they had done to the prole woman in the backyard. He noticed that the light seemed too strong for nine o'clock – twenty-one hours – which was what the clock on the shelf said. He wondered whether he and Julia had slept around the clock and had thought it was twenty-thirty when really they had woken at eight-thirty the next morning.

Mr Charrington came into the room. He looked different. He saw the pieces of the glass paperweight on the floor. "Pick up those pieces," he said sharply.

A man bent down to obey him. Mr Charrington's voice was

different. He did not sound like a prole now. Winston suddenly realized it was his voice that they had heard from the telescreen. Mr Charrington was still wearing his old jacket, but his hair, which had been almost white, was now black, and he was not wearing his glasses. He looked at Winston once and then did not look at him again. He no longer looked like the same person. He was standing straight and he seemed to have grown bigger. His face was now the cold, hard face of a man of about thirty-five years old. Winston realized, for the first time in his life, that he was sure he was looking at a member of the Thought Police.

CHAPTER FIFTEEN
The Ministry of Love

Winston did not know where he was. He supposed he was in the Ministry of Love, but there was no way of being certain. He was alone in a high windowless **cell**. Bright white light came from somewhere and there was a hard, narrow shelf to sit on, fixed to the wall. At the opposite end to the door, there was a toilet without a seat. There were four telescreens, one on each wall.

Winston was hungry, so hungry that his stomach hurt. He had no idea how long he had been there. And he still did not know whether it had been morning or evening when they arrested him. He had not been given any food. He had already learned to sit very still on the narrow shelf. He had felt in his pocket to see if he had anything to eat, but a voice had shouted from the telescreen, "6079, Smith W! Keep your hands out of your pockets in the cells!"

Before being brought here, he had been taken to a noisy, dirty prison where there were Party prisoners like him and also ordinary criminals. The Party prisoners were frightened and silent, but the ordinary criminals shouted at the guards and fought with them. Winston did not know how long they had kept him there. There were no clocks and there was no daylight. Nobody spoke to him.

It might have been two or three hours since they had brought him to this cell. The pain in his stomach never went away.

Sometimes it got worse and he could only think about his desire for food. Sometimes it got better and he started to feel terror about being tortured. He could feel truncheons hitting his elbows and knees as if it was really happening. He did not think about Julia. More often he wondered where he was, and what time of day it was. In this place, he knew the lights would never be turned off. It was the place with no darkness which he had dreamed about and which O'Brien knew about, too.

Suddenly, there was the sound of heavy boots and the door opened. A guard pushed Parsons into the cell. Winston was so surprised that he spoke without thinking about the telescreen.

"*You!*" he cried.

Parsons looked neither interested nor surprised. He was just very unhappy.

"What are you in here for?" asked Winston.

"Thoughtcrime!" replied Parsons, almost crying. "You don't think they'll shoot me, do you, old friend? They don't shoot you if you haven't actually done anything, do they? If you've only had thoughts which you can't help? I tried to do my best for the Party, didn't I?"

"Are you guilty?" said Winston.

"Of course I'm guilty!" cried Parsons, looking at the telescreen. "Thoughtcrime is a terrible thing, old friend. You do it without even knowing you're doing it. Do you know what I said in my sleep? 'Down with Big Brother!'"

"Who told the Thought Police?" asked Winston.

"My little daughter," said Parsons, sounding sad and proud at the same time. "She listened outside the bedroom door. I'm proud of her, really. I've made her into a good little Party member, haven't I?"

Sometime later Parsons was taken away by two guards. More prisoners came and went, mysteriously. Often, an officer pointed at somebody and said, "Room 101".

Winston soon realized that these words filled everyone with terror. They shook, their faces went pale and one man started to shout, "Shoot me! Hang me! Tell me who you want me to betray and I will betray them! Kill my wife and children in front of me! But don't take me to Room 101!"

A long time passed, and Winston was on his own again. When he stood up, he felt as if he was going to faint from hunger. When he sat on the hard shelf, his bones hurt. But when he forgot about how his body felt, the terror returned.

The sound of boots approached again. The door opened and O'Brien came in. Winston jumped to his feet in surprise. "They've got you, too!" he cried.

"They got me a long time ago," said O'Brien, smiling slightly. He moved a little so Winston could see a huge guard with a long black truncheon in his hand. "You knew this, Winston," O'Brien continued. "You have always known it."

Winston realized that he *had* always known it. But there was no time to think about it now. He was looking at the guard's truncheon and wondering where it was going to land.

The truncheon hit Winston's elbow very hard and pain exploded in his body. As he fell to the floor, he saw the guard laughing.

———

It was after this that the **interrogations** started. Winston was tortured and made to confess to a lot of different crimes like spying and betraying secrets to the enemy. There were always six men in black uniforms, sometimes hitting him with their truncheons, sometimes kicking him. Sometimes, he was put back in the cell and left to recover for a few hours, then taken out and beaten again. Sometimes, men in white coats checked his body and gave him pills to make him sleep. In the end, all he wanted to do was find out what they wanted him to confess so he could confess it quickly before the torture started again.

All through his interrogations, although he had never seen him, he had the feeling that O'Brien was there. It was O'Brien who told the guards to hit Winston and it was O'Brien who stopped them from killing him. He was an enemy, then he was a friend. He thought he heard O'Brien's voice in his ear saying, "Don't worry, Winston, I am looking after you. I have been watching you for seven years. Now I am going to **cure** you and make you perfect." It was the same voice that had said to him, *"We shall meet in the place where there is no darkness,"* in his dream.

When Winston was at last conscious again, he was tied to a sort of bed so that he could not move. He did not know how long the interrogations had gone on. He did not know whether the spaces between his memories lasted weeks or just days or even seconds. Since the moment they had arrested him, he had not seen darkness or daylight. Now, light that seemed stronger than usual was falling on his face. O'Brien was standing at his side. Winston did not know how long he had been there. He lay on the bed, looking up at O'Brien. Under O'Brien's hand, there was a **lever**, and below the lever was a **dial**, like an old clock face with numbers.

"I told you," said O'Brien, "that if we met again, it would be here."

"Yes," said Winston.

O'Brien's hand moved the lever slightly and pain exploded through Winston's body. He felt as if his back was going to break.

"You are afraid," said O'Brien, "that your back is going to break. That is what you are thinking, isn't it, Winston?"

Winston did not answer. O'Brien moved the lever again and the pain disappeared. "That was forty," said O'Brien. "The numbers on the dial go up to a hundred. Now, we are going to have a conversation. Remember that if you tell me any lies or say anything stupid, you will cry out with pain. Do you understand that?"

"Yes," said Winston.

O'Brien's voice became gentler. "I am going to cure you," he said, "because it is clear that you are not going to cure yourself. You know what the problem is – you cannot remember real events, and you make yourself think that you remember other events which never happened. Let us think about an example. At the moment, who is Oceania at war with?"

"With Eastasia."

"Good," said O'Brien. "And Oceania has always been at war with Eastasia, hasn't it?"

Winston looked at the dial and did not speak.

"I want the truth, please, Winston. Your truth. Tell me what you think you remember."

"I remember that until only a week before I was arrested, we were not at war with Eastasia. The war against Eurasia had lasted for four years. Before that –"

O'Brien waved his hand and stopped him from speaking. "Let me give you another example," he said. "A few years ago you believed that three Party members who were executed for betraying Oceania to an enemy were not guilty. You believed that you had a photograph which proved this."

Suddenly Winston could see that O'Brien was holding the photograph of the three men. For a moment, he forgot the dial. "It exists!" he cried.

"No," said O'Brien. Then he walked across the room to a memory hole and put the photograph into it. "It does not exist. It never existed."

"But it did exist! It exists in memory. I remember it. You remember it."

"I do not remember it," said O'Brien.

This was doublethink. Winston felt helpless.

O'Brien went on. "There is a Party slogan about control of the past. Repeat it, please."

" '*Whoever controls the past controls the future; whoever controls the present controls the past,*' " said Winston, obeying him immediately.

O'Brien repeated the slogan and then asked, "Do you think, Winston, that the past is something real?"

Winston's eyes moved towards the dial. He did not know whether the answer 'yes' or 'no' would save him from pain.

"No," he said.

"Then where does the past exist?"

"It is written down in records," replied Winston, "and it is in people's memories."

"Well, we, the Party, control all records," said O'Brien, "and we control all memories. So we control the past, don't we?"

"But how can you stop people remembering things?" cried Winston, forgetting the dial. "How can you control memory? You haven't controlled mine!"

O'Brien sounded angry and disappointed. "*You* have not controlled your memory. You have not learned that reality exists only in the mind of the Party and nowhere else. The Party decides what is real and unreal, true and untrue." Then O'Brien asked, "Do you remember writing in your diary, *'Freedom is the freedom to say that two plus two make four'*?"

"Yes," said Winston.

O'Brien held up his left hand so Winston could see only the four fingers. "How many fingers am I holding up?" he asked.

"Four," replied Winston.

"And if the Party says I am holding up five fingers, how many fingers am I holding up?"

"Four," replied Winston.

The word ended in Winston's cry of pain as the dial went up to fifty-five. O'Brien watched him, then pulled the lever back slightly. The pain became less fierce, but it did not go away. O'Brien was still holding his hand up.

"How many fingers?"

"Four."

The dial went up to sixty.

"How many fingers, Winston?"

"Four! What else can I say? Four!"

The pain increased. O'Brien's hand seemed to shake in front of Winston's eyes, but still he saw four fingers.

"How many fingers, Winston?"

"Four! Stop the pain! Four! Four!"

"How many fingers, Winston?"

"Five, five, five."

"No, Winston, you are lying. You still think there are four. How many fingers, please?"

"Four! Five! Any number you like, but stop the pain!"

Suddenly, he was sitting up with O'Brien's arm around his shoulders. Tears were falling down his cheeks. He did not remember O'Brien untying him from the bed so that he could sit up.

"You are a slow learner, Winston," said O'Brien.

Then, he was lying down again and the lever was moving again. The dial must have been on seventy, seventy-five. Still there were four fingers in front of Winston. "I would see five if I could," he cried.

"How many fingers, Winston?" said O'Brien, and the dial went up to eighty.

"I don't know. Four, five, six – I really don't know."

"That's better," said O'Brien. "You must understand that we will change you, Winston. We will make your mind empty and then we will fill it with all the things that the Party believes. And we will keep you alive till you yourself decide to believe in them. We will make you one of us before we kill you."

O'Brien showed Winston two small damp pieces of cloth,

which he then put on either side of Winston's forehead. "This time it will not hurt," he said quite kindly, as Winston's body went stiff, ready for more pain. At that moment, there was a bright white light and Winston felt as if the inside of his head had exploded, although there was no pain. Afterwards, he remembered who he was and where he was, but his head seemed to have an empty space inside it. It was as if a piece of his brain had been removed.

O'Brien held up his hand again. "There are five fingers here. Do you see five fingers?"

And Winston did see them for a moment. "Yes," he replied.

"You see now," said O'Brien, "that it is possible for you to learn. And before we finish for today, have you got any questions?"

"What have you done with Julia?" Winston asked.

O'Brien smiled. "It was a very straightforward interrogation. She betrayed you immediately, Winston. You would not recognize her now – her anger against the Party, her desire for sex and her stupid ideas are all gone."

"Did you torture her?" asked Winston.

O'Brien did not answer. "Next question," he said.

"Does Big Brother exist?"

"Of course he exists. The Party exists. Big Brother *is* the Party."

"Does he exist in the same way that I exist?"

"You do not exist, Winston," replied O'Brien. "Next question."

"What is in Room 101?" asked Winston.

"You know what is in Room 101," replied O'Brien. "Everyone knows what is in Room 101."

CHAPTER SIXTEEN

Freedom is slavery — slavery is freedom

Winston did not know how much time had passed, but he knew that things were a little easier now. He still had to lie flat on the bed, but he was not tied to it so tightly. The dial was rarely turned up very high. Also, he knew that if he avoided giving stupid answers, O'Brien would not turn the dial at all.

"There are three stages which you have to go through," O'Brien said. "You have to learn, then understand and then accept. You have gone through the learning stage. It is time for the second stage. Do you remember writing in your diary, *'I understand HOW: I do not understand WHY'*? You repeated it after you had read part of Goldstein's book."

"Have you read the book?" asked Winston.

"I wrote it," said O'Brien. "At least, I was one of the writers. No book is written by one person alone."

"Is what the book says right?" asked Winston.

"The book describes how the Party controls everything and everyone correctly," replied O'Brien. "But the plan it describes is nonsense. The proles will never start a revolution. No one will ever overthrow the Party. The Party will rule forever." He came closer to the bed. "Now let's think – you understand *how* the Party stays in power. Now give me your answer to the question, '*Why* does the Party want to be in power?'"

"For our own **good**," said Winston. Suddenly, he felt pain through his whole body as O'Brien moved the lever up.

"That was a stupid thing to say, Winston!" he said. "You should know better by now. Now I will tell you the answer," he continued. "The Party does not rule over you for your own good. Rulers or parties who take over countries usually say they want people to be happier, or they want to protect the weak from the strong, or they want everybody to be free and equal. They believe, or want to believe, that they will give power back to the people when they have done these things. But we are different. We just want power – forever.

"You know the Party slogan, '*FREEDOM IS SLAVERY*'," he went on. "Have you ever thought that we can change it to '*SLAVERY IS FREEDOM*'? One person who is free can never win on his or her own because in the end every human being dies. But a person who lets the Party control him or her completely *is* the Party. This person will be free – he or she will never really die because the Party will live forever. It has power over everything – over **matter** in all its forms, over the body, and most importantly, over the mind."

Winston forgot the dial again. He tried to sit up but could not. "But you can't control matter," he cried. "You can't control the weather or diseases or death. You can't control the laws of nature. The earth existed for millions of years before there were men."

O'Brien just waved his hand as if what Winston said was unimportant, and continued, "We control matter because we control the mind. Reality is *inside* your head. Forget what you have learned about history. The earth is only as old as the human mind. Things like the bones of dead animals in rocks were all invented in the nineteenth century. The stars are just bits of fire a few kilometres away. The Party could put them out if it wanted to. Of course, it is also useful sometimes to say the stars are thousands and thousands of kilometres away. But that is why we have doublethink."

Although Winston knew that what O'Brien was saying was nonsense, as usual there was nothing he could do or say against the force of this man who was not only mad, but also intelligent. As Winston listened, he felt as if he was getting smaller and smaller. He felt helpless.

"But all of this is not important," said O'Brien. "The real power we have to fight for is not power over matter, but over people." He paused, and then, sounding like a schoolteacher, he asked, "How does one man get power over another one, Winston?"

Winston thought about this, then he answered, "By hurting him, and by making him fear being hurt again."

"Yes," replied O'Brien. "By making him afraid. Power is in making people afraid. Power is in tearing minds to pieces and putting them together again in new shapes. In the world we are creating, there will be only fear, anger and hate. There will be no love between child and parent, and between man and man, and between man and woman. There will be no love except love of Big Brother. There will be no culture and no science. But there will always be power. If you want a picture of the future, imagine a boot kicking a human face – forever."

He paused as though he expected Winston to speak. But Winston could not say anything. His heart seemed to be frozen.

O'Brien went on, "You are beginning, I can see, to realize what the world will be like. But in the end, you will do more than understand it. You will accept it, welcome it, become part of it."

Winston managed to speak. "You can't succeed," he said weakly.

"Why not?"

"I don't know," said Winston. "You will fail. Something will defeat you. Life will defeat you."

"But we control life, Winston," replied O'Brien. "So what will defeat us?"

"I don't know. People – humans."

Suddenly Winston was no longer tied to the bed. "Get up," O'Brien said. "Imagine that you're the last man against the Party. You are the last example of a human. You will see yourself. Take off your clothes."

Winston untied the bit of string that held his overalls together and they fell off. Beneath his overalls were dirty, torn pieces of his underwear, which he removed. He saw that there was a mirror at the end of the room and approached it, then stopped, hearing himself cry out.

"Go on," said O'Brien. "Stand in front of the mirror. And don't forget to look at yourself from the side as well."

Winston had stopped because the horrible sight of his body shocked him. Then he moved closer to the mirror and looked at his face. He could see the bones under the lined, grey skin. He had very little hair. The skin of the rest of his body was grey, too, and under the dirt he could see red wounds. But the truly frightening thing was how thin he was. He could see all his bones, and his legs were so thin that his knees were wider than his thighs. From the side he could see that his back was bent as if his head was too heavy for his body.

O'Brien got hold of Winston's shoulder and pulled him round so that they were face-to-face.

"Look!" he said. "Even your hair is coming out." He pulled out a handful of hair and showed it to him. "Now open your mouth," he continued. "How many teeth did you have when you came to us? You've only got eleven now. And these are falling out of your head. Look here!" He got hold of one of Winston's front teeth between his powerful thumb and first finger. Pain went through Winston's jaw as O'Brien pulled the loose tooth out. O'Brien threw it across the room.

"Now turn round and look into that mirror again," O'Brien said. "Do you see that thing in front of you? That is what the last man looks like. If you are human, that is what being human looks like. Now put your clothes on again."

As Winston slowly pulled on his clothes, he felt old and weak and suddenly very sorry for himself. He fell on to a small chair and tears started to fall. He cried and cried. O'Brien put a hand on his shoulder, almost kindly.

"It will not last forever," he said. "You can escape from it when you choose to."

"You made me like this," cried Winston.

"No, Winston, *you* did it to yourself when you decided to act against the Party," said O'Brien. "You have seen your body. Your mind looks the same. We have beaten you."

Winston had stopped crying. He thought of Julia. He had

confessed everything about their relationship. He had told them everything he knew about her, but he had not stopped loving her. He looked up at O'Brien.

"I have not betrayed Julia," he said.

O'Brien looked down at him thoughtfully. "No, that is perfectly true," he said. "You have not betrayed Julia."

"Tell me," Winston said, "how soon will they shoot me?"

"You're difficult," said O'Brien. "It might take a long time to make you love the Party. But don't give up hope. Everyone is cured sooner or later. And in the end, we will shoot you."

CHAPTER SEVENTEEN

Room 101

Winston was much better. Weeks or months must have passed. The cell was quite comfortable, with a pillow, sheets and a blanket on the bed, and a small chair. They allowed him to wash himself sometimes in a small metal bowl. They even gave him warm water to wash with. They had given him new underwear and some clean overalls. They had pulled out the rest of his teeth and given him some false ones. He was getting regular meals.

At first, he had spent most of his time lying on his bed asleep. He dreamed a lot during this time, and his dreams were always happy. He was in the Golden Country with his mother, with Julia, or with O'Brien – not doing anything, just sitting in the sun, talking about peaceful things. When he was awake, he did not really think about anything. He was not bored, he was happy to be alone. It was enough not to be tortured or questioned, to have good food to eat and to be clean.

As time passed, he spent less time asleep, but he still did not feel like getting up from the bed. Then he could feel himself getting stronger. Finally, he started to believe that he really was healthier, and he started to do some exercise. In a little while he could walk three kilometres, which he measured by walking around his cell. As he got stronger, his mind started to work again. He had been given a small white board and a pencil, which for a long time he did not touch. Now he sat down on the bed with the board on his knees and he started to teach himself to be a good member of the Party. He began to write down his thoughts, trying to teach his mind to think correctly and to stop thinking the wrong things. All the time, however, with one part of his mind, he wondered how soon they would shoot him.

Then something terrible happened. He was dreaming. He was happy, healthy and strong. He was in the Golden Country, following a path across a field. He could feel the grass under his feet and the gentle sunshine on his face. At the edge of the field, he could see the place where the bird had sung. Suddenly, he was awake, sitting up in bed, and filled with terror. He had heard himself cry aloud, "Julia! Julia! Julia, my love! Julia!"

Winston lay back on the bed. What had he done? They would start torturing him again. He would have to start all over again. For the first time, he realized that he must not only think the correct things, but also, he must feel correctly and he must dream correctly. And all the time he must keep his hate locked inside him without being conscious that it was there. Finally, they would shoot him, and just before the bullet hit him, he would be conscious of his hate. If he could be sure of hating them as he died, he would still be free.

There was the sound of boots outside the cell. The door opened and O'Brien walked in. Behind him were black-uniformed guards.

"Get up," said O'Brien. "Come here."

Winston stood opposite him. O'Brien took Winston's shoulders between his strong hands and looked at him closely.

"You are being stupid," he said. "You are improving; you are thinking in the right way now. But you have failed to make progress with the way that you feel." O'Brien was speaking quite gently to Winston. "Tell me, Winston, and remember, don't lie to me. You know that I always know if you are lying. What are your true feelings towards Big Brother?"

"I hate him."

"You hate him. Good. Then the time has come for you to take the last step. You must love Big Brother. It is not enough to obey him. You must love him."

He pushed Winston towards the guards.

"Room 101," he said.

———

Winston was in a cell which was bigger than most of the ones he had been in. But he did not notice that. All he noticed was that there were two small tables in front of him. One was quite close to him, the other was further away, near the door. He was sitting on a chair, tied to it so tightly that he could not move anything. Something was holding his head so that he could only look straight in front of him. For a moment he was alone, then the door opened and O'Brien came in.

"You asked me once what was in Room 101," he said. "I told you that you knew the answer already. Everyone knows it. The thing that is in Room 101 is the worst thing in the world."

The door opened again. A guard came in, carrying something. He put it down on the table near the door and because of where O'Brien was standing, Winston could not see what it was.

"Everyone has a worst thing in the world," said O'Brien. "For some people it may be death by fire, or by drowning or by being buried alive."

He had moved slightly to one side, so that Winston had a better view of the thing on the table. It was a cage with a sort of mask at one end of it. In the cage, which was divided into two, there were two animals. They were rats.

"For you, the worst thing in the world is rats," O'Brien went on.

Immediately Winston understood how the cage worked. The end with the mask could be put over a person's head, then a door in one of the sides of the cage could be opened so the rats could get to the person's face.

"You can't do that!" he cried out in terror. Then he tried to get control of his voice. "You know that this is not necessary. What do you want me to do or say?"

"Do you remember those horrible dreams when you were standing in front of a wall of darkness, knowing there was something terrifying on the other side?" said O'Brien. "It was the rats which were there."

He picked up the cage and brought it across to the table near Winston. "Rats," said O'Brien, using his schoolteacher's voice, "are meat eaters. In some parts of the city, mothers won't leave babies alone in their houses, even for five minutes. The rats are certain to attack them. In a short time they will eat everything except the bones. They will also attack sick or dying people."

Winston heard himself make a terrible noise. O'Brien picked up the cage and moved it nearer to Winston. It was less than a metre from his face. There was a short, sharp sound.

"I have pressed the first lever," said O'Brien. "You understand how this cage is made. The mask will fit over your head. When I press the other lever, the door of the cage will slide up. These hungry rats will come out of it like bullets. They will jump on to your face and start eating it. Sometimes they attack the eyes first. Sometimes they go straight through the cheeks and start eating the tongue."

The cage was coming nearer. Suddenly the horrible smell of the big brown rats reached Winston's nose and he almost fainted. For a moment, he was mad with terror. Then he had an idea. He must put another human being, the *body* of another human being between himself and the rats.

The mask was coming closer to his face. He could feel it on his cheek. Suddenly he was shouting wildly, over and over again. "Do it to Julia! Do it to Julia! Not me! Julia! I don't care what you do to her. Tear her face off! Not me! Julia! Not me!"

He was falling backwards into blackness, falling through the floor, falling away, away, away from the rats. But O'Brien was still standing at his side. However, through the darkness, he heard a short, sharp sound, and knew that the cage door would not open.

CHAPTER EIGHTEEN
2 + 2 = 5

Winston sat alone in a corner of a café, where he sat every day from fifteen hours. Opposite him, there was a poster of Big Brother and on the table there was a glass of Victory Gin. When he finished it, a waiter would fill the glass again. He hated the taste of it, but he depended on it. It sent him to sleep at night, and by his bed there was a bottle of it which he drank from every morning so that he could get up. His face was fat and red and no one ever came to sit with him. But he was a free man and no one was interested in him. He did a meaningless job in the Ministry of Truth working on the eleventh edition of the Newspeak Dictionary. Although he did the job for only a few hours a week, he was paid more than for doing his old job.

Winston's eyes were on the telescreen because he was waiting for news of the war with Eurasia. Oceania had always been at war with Eurasia. Winston felt both excited and worried about the war because there were serious problems in Africa. He was expecting bad news – a Eurasian victory would be terrible for Oceania. As he waited for the news, his finger wrote $2 + 2 = 5$ in the dust on the table, and his mind went back to his meeting with Julia.

He had seen her and had spoken to her only once since they had let him leave the Ministry of Love. It was by accident in a park on a bitterly cold day in March. He saw her ahead of him and immediately realized that she had changed in some way.

It seemed as if they were going to walk past each other without speaking, but he turned and walked beside her, without really wanting to talk to her. She was pale and there was a red mark across her forehead as if she had been injured. But that was not the change in her. It was when Winston put his arm around her waist that he realized what had changed – she felt thicker and her body was stiff under her clothes. It felt as if it was a dead body. She did not seem to notice his arm around her. He did not try to kiss her.

As they walked across the grass, she looked at him, without speaking. It was a look of dislike. They sat down on metal chairs, side by side, and at last she spoke.

"I betrayed you," she said.

"I betrayed you," he answered.

She gave him another look of dislike. "Sometimes," she said, "they say they will do something terrible to you. And then you say, 'Don't do it to me, do it to somebody else, do it to this person or that person.' And you might say, afterwards, that it was only a trick and you said it just to make them stop and didn't really mean it. But that isn't true. At the time when it happens, you mean it. You think there's no other way of saving yourself, and you're ready to save yourself that way. You want it to happen to the other person. You don't care what they suffer. All you care about is yourself."

"All you care about is yourself," he repeated.

"And after that," she continued, "you don't feel the same towards the other person any longer."

"No," he said, "you don't feel the same."

There was nothing more to say. The wind blew their thin overalls against their bodies. They became embarrassed to sit in silence and it was too cold to keep still. She said something about catching a bus and stood up to go.

"We must meet again," he said.

"Yes," she said, "we must meet again."

She walked away and soon Winston could not tell which person she was on the street. Perhaps it was no longer possible to recognize her from behind because of her thick, stiff body.

"At the time when it happens," she had said, "you mean it." *She* had meant it. He had not just said it, *he* had meant it. He had meant that she and not he should be –

The music from the telescreen changed and Winston stopped thinking about the meeting with Julia. He picked up his glass and held it up to his nose. The gin became more horrible every time he drank it.

Without meaning to, Winston suddenly remembered a time when he was a boy. It was a grey, rainy day and they were at home. He and his sister had been fed up, then his mother had got out a board game. He played games with his mother and they laughed and laughed. His tiny sister, who was too young to understand the game, laughed because they were laughing. For a whole afternoon, they had all been happy together. It was about a month before his mother disappeared.

Suddenly, the sound of exciting military music came from the telescreen. Winston came back to the present and started watching the telescreen again. This would be the news about the war. It was going to be good news because this kind of music always announced a victory. An excited voice started speaking, but Winston could not hear it very well because people were shouting and cheering outside. He heard bits of the announcement: "a great victory – Eurasia beaten – control of the whole of Africa – Oceania safe – half a million prisoners – nearly the end of the war – the greatest victory in the history of the world!"

Winston looked at the poster of Big Brother. Ten minutes ago, when he was waiting for news about the war, he had still doubted what he felt about Big Brother. But he had changed! A lot had changed in him during his time in the Ministry of Love, but now the final change took place. Winston felt he was in the Ministry of Love again. He knew that he had been forgiven. He saw himself at his trial, confessing everything, betraying everybody. He could feel himself walking down a white corridor and into sunlight, a guard with a gun behind him. The bullet which he had been waiting for was at last entering his brain.

Winston looked up at the huge face of Big Brother. Two tears fell down his face. Everything was all right. He had won the victory over himself. He loved Big Brother.

During-reading questions

Write the answers to these questions in your notebook.

CHAPTERS ONE AND TWO

1 What do you learn about Winston Smith in Chapter One? Think about his age and looks, his job, where he lives, and what he feels about his life.

2 What do you learn about children in Oceania in Chapter Two?

3 What does Winston remember about O'Brien? How does he feel about him?

CHAPTERS THREE AND FOUR

1 What is Winston's job and how is it connected with doublethink?

2 Who is Syme and what do you learn about him?

3 What does Winston notice in the canteen that makes him afraid?

CHAPTER FIVE

1 Why is a photo from a newspaper important to Winston?

2 Winston writes this in his diary: *Freedom is the freedom to say that two plus two make four. If that is allowed, then everything else follows.* What does he mean?

CHAPTER SIX

1 What do you learn about Mr Charrington and his shop?

2 Who does Winston see on his walk after he leaves the shop and how does he feel?

CHAPTER SEVEN

1 How does the young woman contact Winston and why?
2 Why does Winston go to the monument in Victory Square?

CHAPTER EIGHT

1 What do you learn about Julia in this chapter?
2 How do you think Winston felt while he was listening to the bird singing?

CHAPTER NINE

1 How does Julia surprise Winston in the room above the shop?
2 How do Julia and Winston feel when Julia sees a rat?

CHAPTERS TEN AND ELEVEN

1 How do you think Winston is feeling during June?
2 What is *it* in this sentence: "It had happened at last."?
3 How are the proles different from the members of the Party, according to Winston, and what makes him realize this?

CHAPTERS TWELVE AND THIRTEEN

1 In what ways is the place where O'Brien lives different from where Winston lives?
2 Why is Winston able to complete the sentence which O'Brien starts: "If we meet again –"?
3 What is Winston given during Hate Week and what does he do with it?

CHAPTER FOURTEEN

1. How do Julia and Winston learn that something terrible is going to happen?
2. Why do you think Winston realizes, for the first time in his life, that he is sure he is looking at a member of the Thought Police?

CHAPTER FIFTEEN

1. Why does O'Brien try to make Winston believe that he is holding up five fingers even though he is holding up four?
2. What do you think O'Brien means when he says to Winston, "You do not exist"?

CHAPTER SIXTEEN

1. How do we know that O'Brien is "not only mad, but also intelligent"?
2. How does O'Brien prove to Winston that the Party has beaten him? And what does Winston say to prove that it hasn't?

CHAPTERS SEVENTEEN AND EIGHTEEN

1. Why is Winston taken to Room 101?
2. How does Winston stop the rats from attacking him?
3. How do you know that the Party has beaten Winston?

After-reading questions

1 Look at your answers to Before-reading questions 2, 3 and 4. How close to correct are your answers? How would you like to change them now?

2 Did the novel end in the way you expected it to? Explain your answer.

3 Who are these characters? What parts do they play in the story?
   a Goldstein
   b Big Brother
   c Parsons
   d Mr Charrington

4 What happens in these places in the story?
   a the corridor outside Winston's flat
   b the canteen in the Ministry of Truth
   c Mr Charrington's shop
   d Room 101

Exercises

1 **Complete these sentences in your notebook, using the correct form of the correct word.**

spy	execute	strike	tool
dust	savage	were	praise	ration

1 From his window, Winston could see ..*dust*.. blowing around in the streets below.

2 Winston knew that keeping a private diary could get him ....

3 If Winston hadn't gone back to work when the clocks .... fourteen, he would have been late.

4 Often children would .... on their parents for the Thought Police.

5 People living in Victory House had to keep their own .... because nobody repaired anything for them.

6 Winston was shocked by how .... the Parsons children were.

7 Children .... often .... in newspaper articles for telling the Thought Police what their parents had done wrong.

8 People have to live on food .... in Oceania.

2 **Complete these sentences in your notebook, using**
could, must **or** *should.*

1 The Golden Country .*must*. have been a real place Winston
had once seen.

2 Winston felt he .... have been able to remember more
about the past.

3 Big Brother .... not have been wrong about the attack by
Eurasian soldiers on Oceanian soldiers, so Winston had to
write a new article.

4 "Comrade Withers .... have been guilty of a terrible
crime," thought Winston.

5 "Tillotson .... have been given the same article to write as
me," thought Winston.

6 Winston .... have shared his razor blades with Syme and
Parsons, but he didn't want to.

7 Winston .... not have refused to give Parsons $2.00 for
Hate Week, or Parsons would have reported him.

8 Winston .... have kept his face calmer when he heard
about the change to the chocolate ration so that nobody
could see his feelings.

3 Complete these sentences in your notebook, using the correct forms of the verbs in brackets.

1 If Winston ...*stay*... (**stay**) with Katherine, he ...*would be*. (**be**) more unhappy now.

2 Winston thought life .... (**be**) the same for the proles if the Great Revolution .... (**not happen**).

3 The three Party members .... (**visit**) New York when they confessed to being in Siberia.

4 Winston .... (**walk**) for a long time before he came across Mr Charrington's shop.

5 If Winston .... (**come back**) to the shop, he .... (**buy**) the picture of the church.

6 "She' .... (**follow**) me since I left work," thought Winston.

4 Write a sentence for each word in your notebook, to show that you understand the meaning.

1 slogan *Before Hate Week, children wrote Party slogans on banners to hang on the fronts of buildings.*

2 banner

3 black market

4 conspiracy

5 exit

6 microphone

7 monument

8 overalls

9 pessimistic

10 victory

CHAPTERS NINE AND TEN

5 **Correct these sentences in your notebook.**

1 Mr Charrington does not know that Winston is planning to meet a woman in the upstairs room. _..knows.._

2 Julia and Winston drink the coffee that Winston has brought.

3 Julia wears make-up and perfume in the little room so that she feels more like a Party member.

4 Winston finds Syme's name on the list of Chess Club members on the work noticeboard.

5 Winston and Julia believe their relationship will last forever.

6 O'Brien mentions Syme's name during his conversation with Winston in the corridor.

CHAPTERS ELEVEN AND TWELVE

6 **Write the correct word in your notebook. Then write a definition.**

1 DEMAIR	*admire*	*to have a high opinion of someone or something*
2 SEFNSOC		
3 NOUSSCIOC		
4 GENLEAT		
5 LPELYESIAC		
6 DEYERG		
7 QUILDI		
8 TARPEASE		

7 Write these sentences in the passive form in your notebook.

1 Children were tearing down the banners while the speech continued.

While the speech continued _the banners were being torn down (by children)_.

2 Julia was not interested in the fact that a man had given Winston Goldstein's book.

Julia was not interested in the fact that Winston ....

3 All the articles that Winston and his colleagues had written contained false information.

All the articles ....

4 Someone was watching Winston and Julia all the time that they were in their room.

All the time that Winston and Julia ....

5 A voice from the telescreen was repeating everything they said.

Everything ....

6 Winston saw that one of the men had hit Julia in her stomach.

Winston saw that Julia ....

8 **Write the correct parts of speech for these words in your notebook.**

1	betrayal (n)	> verb:	*betray.*
2	explode (v)	> noun:	....
3	frozen (adj)	> verb:	....
4	interrogation (n)	> verb:	....
5	invent (v)	> noun:	....
6	memory (n)	> adjective:	....
7	mysteriously (adv)	> noun:	....
8	terror (n)	> adjective:	....

9 **Write the correct words to complete these sentences in your notebook.**

1 At first, Winston **would** / **will** spend most of his time lying on his bed asleep.

2 Winston **would** / **could** rather sleep than do any exercise.

3 For a while Winston felt **too** / **quite** happy in his cell.

4 He **would** / **should** sit every day in a café from fifteen hours.

5 Winston was **so** / **such** terrified by the rats that he betrayed Julia.

6 "I wish that I **hadn't** / **haven't** seen Julia again," thought Winston.

7 Finally Winston had had **too much** / **quite much** pain – and in the end he loved Big Brother.

Project work

1 You are writing a history book about the Party many years after the power of the Party has ended. Choose at least six of the topics (a–k) and write a short paragraph on each, explaining what they are and how they fit into the world of *Nineteen-Eighty Four*:

   a Big Brother
   b Hate Week
   c Daily life for Outer Party members
   d Daily life for Inner Party members
   e The Records Department
   f Room 101
   g Goldstein and the Brotherhood
   h The Four Ministries
   i The Spies
   j The Thought Police
   k The war

2 You have a job working on the Newspeak Dictionary. Re-read what Syme says about his work in Chapter Four.

   a Write definitions of these words. You can choose to write in Oldspeak or Newspeak.

   > facecrime   memory hole   prole   speakwrite
   > telescreen   thoughtcrime   to vaporize   doubleplusungood

   b Invent six new Newspeak words and write definitions for them.

3 Winston knows that he will be executed at some point after he has been completely beaten by the Party. Write an article about him for the *Times* newspaper which might have been written by someone doing the job Winston did at the Ministry of Truth. The article describes Winston before he is arrested by the Thought Police. To get some ideas, re-read the beginning of Winston's article about Comrade Ogilvy (in Chapter Four).

4 Re-read the section about Winston finding the photo of the three important Party members who had been executed (page 38, from "In the years . . ." to "maybe by being tortured.") Either write a script for the scene at the trial of the three Party members OR write a script for a television report which appeared after the trial. You can work as a group to create your script and perform it.

5 Choose four key events from the story that you did not read about in Winston's diary and write his diary entries for them.

Essay questions

1 How is technology used in *Nineteen Eighty-Four*? Do you recognize any similarities between its use in the story and the use of technology now? (500 words)

2 Compare the ways Julia and Winston feel and behave. Then give your opinions about their differences. For example, do you have more sympathy for one character than the other? (500 words)

3 "*Nineteen Eighty-Four* is not dystopian fiction. In fact, it holds a mirror up to the modern world." Do you agree? Explain why or why not. (500 words)

Glossary

alcove (n.)
a place where a wall is further back than the rest of the wall

anti- (prefix)
thinking that something is wrong or bad

article (n.)
a news story in a newspaper

banner (n.)
a long piece of card or material that has pictures or writing on it. People sometimes carry banners to show what they believe in.

betray (v.); **betrayal** (n.)
when you break a promise you made to someone or you tell other people about their secret. When you *betray* someone, it is a *betrayal*.

black market (n.)
when people buy and sell things that are difficult to get, they do it on the *black market*. The person selling the things has usually got them in a way that is not honest.

canteen (n.)
a place in an office building, school, etc. where people buy and eat food

cell (n.)
a small room in a prison where people sleep

community centre (n.)
a building where people go to meet each other and talk, have a drink, play games, etc.

comrade (n.)
a word used for speaking to or about members of a political *party* by other members of the same party. It is usually used by members of the Communist Party.

conscious (adj.)
knowing about something and being able to understand it

conspiracy (n.)
a secret plan to harm someone or something

coral (n.)
pink, white and other coloured rock-like forms under the sea. *Coral* is made from the bones of very small sea animals.

correction (n.)
a small change that you make in a document, *article*, etc.

cubicle (n.)
a small space that is separate from the rest of a room

cure (v.)
to do something that makes someone well again after they have been ill or hurt

dare (v.)
to do something that might have a bad result

denounce (v.)
to tell someone (often the police, media, etc.) that a person has done something bad

department (n.)
a part of an organization that does a particular type of work

dial (n.)
a round object on a machine with a *needle* (= long thin part) that moves around to show an amount of something

dust (n); **dusty** (adj.)
dust is very small pieces of dirt. If a place is *dusty*, there are lots of small pieces of dirt on everything.

edition (n.)
one of the copies of a newspaper or book. A new *edition* is printed when changes are made.

execute (v.)
to kill someone because they have done something wrong. Some countries *execute* criminals.

exist (v.)
to be real or alive in this world

fiction (n.)
stories that are made up or invented

frame (n.)
a thing that you put a picture in before you hang it on a wall. *Frames* can be made of wood, metal or plastic. A *frame* is also the wood around the glass in a window.

freedom (n.)
Freedom is when people can do what they want and say what they want. *Freedom* is the noun of *free*.

furnace (n.)
a container with a very large, hot fire inside it

generation (n.)
all the people who are about the same age. A *generation* is also the length of time that it takes for children to become adults and have their own children.

gin (n.)
an alcoholic drink that is strong and has no colour

good (n.)
If someone does something for your own *good*, they do it to help you or to improve your life.

gram (n.)
We use *grams* as a way of measuring the weight of something. There are 1,000 *grams* in a kilogram.

hanging (n.)
in this story, when someone kills a person by putting something around their neck and holding them above the ground

ignorance (n.)
when people do not know about something

inner (adj.)
in this story, belonging to the group of people in an organization who control it. They usually belong to the *Inner Party* or *inner* circle.

instruction (n.)
clear spoken or written information telling you what to do and how to do it

interrogation (n.)
asking someone a lot of questions because you think they have done something wrong. This situation is called an *interrogation*.

lever (n.)
a long handle that you pull to make a machine work

mask (n.)
something that you wear over your face to make you look different

matter (n.)
the material that all things are made from

microphone (n.)
People speak into microphones to make their voices louder. They are also used to record what someone is saying.

ministry (n.)
a government *department* that does a particular type of work

monument (n.)
something that is built to remind people of an important person or something important that happened

national anthem (n.)
a country's song. It is played at international sports games or when a king, queen, president, etc. visits.

no longer (adv.)
If something *no longer* happens, it used to happen but it does not happen now.

offence (n.)
something that a law says you must not do. It is an *offence* to kill someone.

outer (adj.)
in this story, belonging to the group
of people in an organization who do
not control it. They are in the *Outer
Party* or *outer* circle.

overalls (n.)
something you wear that is like a
shirt and trousers joined together.
You wear *overalls* over other clothes
to protect them if you are working
with, for example, paint or oil.

overthrow (v.)
to use force to stop a government or
leader from having control

paperweight (n.)
a heavy object made of, for example,
glass or metal, used to hold loose
papers down

party (n.)
a political group

patrol (n)
a group of police officers who go
around an area regularly to make
sure there is no trouble

perfume (n.)
a liquid that women put on their
skin to make them smell nice

pessimistic (adj.)
believing that only bad things will
happen

pipe (n.)
Water moves through *pipes* in a
building and under the ground.

power (n.)
being able to control what happens
or what people do

praise (v. and n.)
You *praise* someone or give someone
praise when you say they have done
something good.

rare (adj.)
difficult to find or get because there
is not much of it

ration (n.)
a controlled amount of something
that each person is allowed to have.
There are usually *rations* when there
is not enough of something, for
example when there is a war.

razor blade (n.)
the piece of sharp thin metal that
removes hair from your skin when
you are shaving

reality (n.)
reality is what is really happening
and what is really true. *Reality* is the
noun of *real*.

rebel (v. and n.)
to *rebel* is to refuse to do what other people tell you to do. Someone who does this is a *rebel*.

record (n.)
information that is kept about people and things

revolution (n.)
when people change the government of their country by fighting against it

risk (v. and n.)
If you *risk* something or take a *risk*, you do something even when something bad might happen because of it.

savage (adj.)
cruel and violent

servant (n.)
a person whose job is to cook and clean in someone's home

shelf (n.)
a flat piece of wood that is attached to a wall. People usually put things on it.

slavery (n.)
when people work very hard for no money and have no control over their own lives

slogan (n.)
in this story, a phrase (= words that are easy to remember) that a political organization uses to show its beliefs

socialism (n.)
when the government owns many of a country's industries and believes that everyone should share equally in a country's wealth

spy (v. and n.)
someone whose job is to find out secrets from their country's enemies. Someone who *spies* has this job.

stove (n.)
something that provides heat for cooking

strike (past tense **struck**) (v.)
When a clock *strikes* 2, 11, etc., it makes two, eleven, etc. sounds to show that it is 2 o'clock, 11 o'clock, etc. If something *strikes* a place, it hits it.

swear (v.)
to say rude words because you are angry

sweat (v. and n.)
to produce small drops of water through your skin because you are hot, ill or frightened. This water that your body produces is called *sweat*.

torture (v. and n.)
when you hurt someone or do bad things to them until they do or say what you want. People are usually *tortured* for information.

truncheon (n.)
a thick stick that is used to hit someone. Police officers carry *truncheons*.

underwear (n.)
the clothes that you wear under your trousers, dress or skirt

vaporize (v.)
to make someone disappear and never be seen again

victory (n.)
when you win a competition or a war

Penguin Readers

Visit **www.penguinreaders.co.uk**
for FREE Penguin Readers resources
and digital and audio versions of this book.